*C. H. Waddington*

# Tools for Thought

Jonathan Cape Thirty Bedford Square London

First published 1977
Copyright © The Estate of the late C. H. Waddington,
and Yolanda Sonnabend
Jonathan Cape Ltd, 30 Bedford Square, London WC1
ISBN 0 224 01077 8

Filmset in 'Monophoto' Ehrhardt
and printed in Great Britain by
Richard Clay (The Chaucer Press) Ltd
Bungay, Suffolk

# Contents

# Publisher's Note

C. H. Waddington died on 26 September 1975 shortly after completing his revision to *Tools for Thought* but before he was able to see proofs. His original plan was to write two books to cover the ideas that had concerned him since the late 1960s. *Tools for Thought* was intended as a popular guide to the new ways of perceiving and thinking about the world and its intended successor, *Man-Made Futures*, was a working out of those ideas in relation to what he called the world problematique, the key ecological and political problems facing Earth. The second book was finished in draft and he was completing revisions when he died. Alas, it has not been possible so far to bring the second book to a sufficient state where publication would be easy.

The present text of *Tools for Thought* has been left untouched except for the deletion of minor references to the second book.

P. M. S. 1977

# Introduction

I doubt if there has ever been a period in history when a greater proportion of people have found themselves frankly puzzled by the way the world reacts to their best efforts to change it, if possible for the better. We knock down some dilapidated slums and put up reasonably smart new buildings in their place, only to find a few years later that the inhabitants of the area are just as badly off and living in as great squalor as before. We lend considerable sums of money to a tropical country and show it how to organize public health, and even provide it with medical staff for some years, and the result is that the level of nutrition falls alarmingly and the babies are dying of starvation, instead of the infectious diseases that killed them before. If things go unexpectedly wrong once or twice, that is, one might say rather paradoxically, only to be expected; but recently they seem to have been going wrong so often and in so many different contexts, that many people are beginning to feel that they must be thinking in some wrong way about how the world works. I believe that this suspicion is probably correct. The ways of looking at things that we have in the past accepted as common sense really do not work under all circumstances, and it is very likely that we have reached a period of history when they do not match the type of processes which are going on in the world at large.

We have been trained to think, or have accepted as common sense, that what goes on around us can usually be understood as some set of simple causal sequences in which, for instance, $a$ causes $b$ and $b$ then causes $c$, then $c$ causes $d$ and so on. This is only good enough when $a$ causes $b$ but has very little other effect on anything else, and similarly the overwhelmingly most important effect of $b$ is to cause $c$. Many of our own individual actions still have this character. That is really because they are in some ways relatively feeble compared to the whole mass of things and processes of which they are a part. The change which has occurred, or is occurring now, is that the effects of human societies on their surroundings are now so powerful that it is no longer adequate to concentrate on the primary effects and neglect all secondary influences. When modern health care is applied to a primitive society, it is so powerful that it is no longer a question only of curing a few cases of illness; it drastically lowers the death rate, particularly of young children, so that the numbers of the population increase rapidly and, of course, demand more food. This effect on agriculture and imports, which is quite secondary, and indeed negligible when medicine was fairly inefficient and applied only on a small scale, becomes of real and possibly decisive importance when the medical work is massive and effective. We can no longer consider the field of medicine as isolated; we have to see it as linked up in a complex with the numbers of the population, the demand for foodstuffs, the sources of paying for foodstuffs, and a whole lot of other factors.

The scale of very many of the impacts of mankind on the world surrounding him is now so great that they go right below the surface of things. At the deeper level, we find that most aspects of life and its interactions with its surroundings are interconnected into complexes. No powerful action can be expected to have only one consequence, confined to the thing it was primarily directed at. It is almost bound to affect lots of other things as well. Our old-fashioned common sense has not had to face such situations before, and is not well adapted to doing so. We need nowadays to be able to think not just about simple processes but about complex systems. Many suggestions have been made, particularly in the last years when the problems have become more pressing, of different ways of trying to do this. This book is an attempt to bring together most of these proposed 'Tools for Thought'. Many of them were originally put forward accompanied by a lavish decoration of technical jargon. Part of this may have been due to the genuine difficulty of finding ways of formulating new ideas; part perhaps for the less excusable reason that it might make the ideas look more profound and novel than they really were. However, any idea that is going to be really useful in this connection can, after adequate time to digest it, be put into reasonably simple language. This book is one of the first that has tried to do this with the whole range of present-day ideas on thinking about complex systems. It demands absolutely no mathematics from its readers, and I think there are not more than two examples of mathematical symbols used in the whole book; and anyone could understand the ideas involved even if he skipped those.

The ideas are in fact explained as far as possible in straightforward English words. However, many people, including myself, find that it is often useful and enlightening to have visual illustrations of ideas. This book is therefore provided with a large number of diagrams. These are not intended to express facts about quantities of things, like the usual graphs one sees in scientific books. They are strictly illustrations of ideas, and their purpose is to stimulate your imagination to seize the gist of what an idea is about. They are therefore not drawn in the way that has become conventional for illustrations in technical or most other intellectual books, but have been executed by someone whose main interests are in painting and design. Yolanda Sonneband is a painter – and there are rather few such, though more than suggested by the old jibe, 'bête comme un peintre' – who combines the intellectual capacity to grasp the ideas with the visual imagination to find a way of symbolizing them in drawings which are always pleasant, and sometimes beautiful.

At the end I have provided a list of books and articles about particular methods, which I hope will be useful both to those who would like a little additional explanation and discussion, and to those who want an indication of how to enter considerably more deeply into particular things which have caught their attention. Section A and part of Section B of Chapter 11 are based on a report written for me by Robin Roy, who is now with the Open University, while he was on my staff at the State University of New York at Buffalo. I am grateful to him for allowing me to use this.

The complexities revealed by the more powerful effects which human societies are now exerting are now only within certain areas, such as food, population and so on. We finally find ourselves driven to realize that each of these major complex areas is in its turn related to the others. We have found ourselves faced by a series of problems – atomic warfare, the population exploion, the food problem, energy, natural resources, pollution and so on – each complex enough in itself, but then it turns out that each of these is only one aspect of, as it were, a Total Problem, in which all aspects of the world's workings are inter-related. One way of beginning to approach it is briefly described in Chapter 12 of this book. This Total Problem is sometimes called the World Problematique.

*Edinburgh, Scotland*                                   C. H. Waddington

# 1 Philosophies

'For Heaven's sake,' you'll say, 'just how systematic do you have to try to be? Let's skip this and get on to something that matters.' Okay, we could, but you'd come back to it. Philosophy does matter. It matters particularly to those – the great majority of mankind – whose life is devoted to bringing about changes of some kind or other in the world surrounding them; even if these effects are of no more import than selling more of Messrs X's refrigerators than Messrs Y succeeds in unloading on to the market. The only people who, to some extent, escape from the domination of a philosophy which they consciously or unconsciously believe in are those few who devote themselves so wholeheartedly to researching into new understandings of human or inanimate nature that the sheer brute facts they come across impose themselves regardless of the philosophical system with which they were approached (see p. 17 ). And there are *very* few, even among the minority who try to do research, who are lucky enough to strike a bonanza which sweeps them off their feet to that extent. For the rest of us, it is just as well to know something of the main alternative philosophies, if only to see why the other chap is talking such nonsense, and why he simply does not seem able to get the drift of what you are saying yourself. It is likely to be not his intelligence, but his philosophy, which is responsible.

Philosophy used to be considered the queen of the sciences, the most genuine expression of the humanness of man. But recently it has fallen on bad days. At present the conventional wisdom of the dominant group (the thirty-eights to fifty-eights) uses two kinds of brush-off. The scientists say: 'All this theorizing is purely speculative. All you need is common sense. Get down to the bench and measure something', and the Arts people say: 'All this theorizing is arid logic-chopping or rococo linguistic elaboration: All you need is common sense. Go out to the arenas of life and feel something!'

Of course both these statements are highly philosophical. What is

FIG. 1a.1

common sense except the philosophy which your parents or your peers have soaked you in when you weren't realizing what you were absorbing? Philosophy of one kind or another cannot be avoided or evaded or given up like sin in Lent. Perhaps the most convincing proof of this is to look at the sad fate of people who have tried to programme computers to see, or to use language, or even eventually to think in ways which they hope would begin to resemble those of the human species. They started off their task with the usual Conventional Wisdom of the Dominant Group* – that we don't have to fuss about philosophy. At the end of ten or fifteen years, and a score or so million American dollars (mostly

* If you would like to contract this lengthy phrase to a set of initials, in the fashionable way, COWDUNG is memorizable, appropriate and accurate enough.

drawn from the US Department of Defense, which might easily have used them for worse purposes), this is just what they are finding they have to fuss about. The only way to make a robot anything more than an adding machine is to provide him with a philosophy. He cannot even see to any purpose, let alone use language, unless there is built into his system some sort of model of the kinds of things or processes that he may expect to encounter.

It's only when someone endows him with a philosophy that a robot begins to get within sight of even the simplest human capabilities. It's no good saying 'Okay, but I've got beyond that stage. I can do without one.' You can't, any more than you can do without your DNA genes, although mankind has in important ways 'gone beyond them'. Some sort of philosophy is a prerequisite for humanity. Where you can do better than the robot is to have either a better philosophy or more of them.

Philosophies do not need to be detailed. In fact if they are too detailed they become counter-productive. The essential function of a philosophy is to provide a mental machinery for dealing with a large variety of things – electro-magnetic vibrations (light), oscillations of air density (sound), chemical substances (smells), pressures (tactile sensations) – and interpreting them into something which has 'meaning', i.e. something to which we respond or react (of the light rays passing through the lens of our eye at any moment we may respond to something between 0 and 5 per cent, but not much more). But there is no reason why we – and I suppose eventually our robots – should not have at our disposal several alternative philosophies, which provide different ways of interpreting chaos into sense. According to COWDUNG, if we deign to notice philosophy at all we ought to choose one or other of a number of conflicting schemes. We will now discuss the main varieties, but it is not quite frivolous to suggest that the best thing to do is to adopt all of them – a bit – so as to have a nice range of tools amongst which you may find something suitable for whichever situation you find yourself dealing with.

## A. Natural Philosophy

Let us start by considering the two great philosophical alternatives which are concerned with the kind of intellectual picture we have of the world of nature – at the moment leaving on one side questions of emotions, morals, etc., which we will discuss in the next section.

One view is that the world essentially consists of *things*, and that any changes we notice are really secondary, arising from the way things interact with one another. The alternative is that the world consists of *processes*, and that the things we discern are only stills out of what is essentially a movie. These alternatives go back to the earliest Greek philosophers who lived before Socrates (about 600–500 BC). The 'thing' view is usually associated with the name of Democritus, who actually used the word 'atom' as the name for the basic things – invisibly small unchangeable and unchanging little lumps of something which could be called matter, though they were not quite the same as what a modern chemist or physicist would call an atom.

The classical spokesman for the other view was Heraclitus, who argued that it is an essential feature of things that they are always in the process of change, like a flame into which burnable substances pass, are burnt, and hot gases come out. You can never step into the same river twice, said Heraclitus, for the water is flowing, and when you step into it again tomorrow it will not be the same water as it was when you stepped in today.

The Democritean 'things' view is the most usual in present-day common sense. A great many of the things we have to deal with do not change their nature much over the period of time with which we are concerned with them. The sun, the moon, the earth and its rocks, do, of course, undergo changes, and when pressed everyone will admit it. But the changes are so slow that for most purposes it is alright to forget them. Again, at the other end of the scale of size, the chemical atoms of iron, carbon, oxygen, sodium and the rest, with which the chemist deals, will not change in their essential nature within any period of time we are normally concerned with. It seems much simpler to regard them not as processes but as things, and to get down to the practical problem of finding out how these things interact with one another, to bring about the essentially secondary processes of chemical reaction. There are, therefore, many contexts in which the 'thing' view is the sensible one to adopt.

It is just in an intermediate range of subjects, between astronomy and geology on the one hand, and chemistry and physics on the other, that the weaknesses of the 'thing' view become apparent; and from many points of view it is just this intermediate range that is the most interesting. If one considers a living creature, for instance, one can take a 'thing' view, and regard it as a set of chemical and physical interactions going on between essentially unchanging things, namely the chemical substances out of which it is built. But this attitude seems less satisfying when applied to a living system than it does when used, for instance, in connection with an industrial plant. Although it may indeed lead us to discover a reasonably good account of how the body works as a machine from minute to minute, taking in food, digesting it, excreting the waste, using the energy of substances it absorbs to carry out various other processes and so on, this does not seem quite enough. In fact, the activities which the body does are usually more interesting in themselves than on account of the nature of the chemical substances used to do them. We are more interested in the fact that muscles can contract to bring about bodily movement than we are in the chemistry by which the contraction is produced. Again, to take another example, not this time from a living system, it is much more interesting to find out what a computer can do than to know what it is made of – whether it is copper, silver, glass, plastic, funny compounds of silicon or what have you. The 'thing' view may be useful to the practical engineer, but does not seem to lead at all directly to the subjects which are of most general interest.

Again, concentrating on the 'thing' aspects of a living system tends to lead one to forget that animals develop; they start as fertilized eggs, go through an elaborate process of developing into an adult form, which usually lasts a reasonably long time, but which is all the while undergoing slow changes, which will lead eventually to old age and death. Further, there is a still slower kind of change, that involved in the evolution of the species from more primitive ancestors, up to the present form, and presumably beyond this into something else. The whole-hearted adoption of the 'thing' view is a temptation to forget these other sorts of change, and to concentrate mainly on finding out how adult bodies work, as though they were no more involved in developmental or evolutionary changes than are automobiles. Its enemies claim that it leads to a garage-mechanic mentality.

During most of this century, the conventional wisdom of the dominant group about the nature of living organisms has been a rather exaggerated form of the 'thing' view; and when this is applied to man and his social affairs, it seems, to me at least, to fall quite appropriately under the heading COWDUNG. It argues that the world and everything in it is constituted from arrangements of essentially unchanging material particles, whose nature has already been largely, if not entirely, discovered by the researches of physics and chemistry. These physico-chemical entities are supposed to constitute the whole of objective reality.

In the early years of the century, this view, when applied to living things, was known as 'mechanism'. The human being was regarded as a very complicated machine, built up of these physico–chemical parts. A few rather eccentric biologists pointed out that there are many properties of living things, such as their development, their evolution, their apparent organization and particularly their consciousness, when one can be certain that that occurs, as it does in ourselves, which are difficult or impossible to explain in terms of arrangements of material particles as those are usually defined by physics and chemistry. It was sometimes claimed that living things must involve some other type of principle, a 'vital force' of some kind. The adherents of this view, known as 'vitalism', were however not able to explain the nature of this force in any terms in which it could be reconciled with the rest of human knowledge. It remained no more than an inexplicable joke. Actually few scientists were ever tempted to believe in it wholeheartedly; but the fiercer believers in mechanism are often tempted to believe that there was a vitalist hiding under the bed of many of their quite respectable, but less doctrinaire, colleagues.

The great advances in our understanding of living things during the first half of this century is evidence of how effectively the 'thing', mechanistic, view can work as a practical recipe for investigating biological processes. It has led to an enormous increase in understanding how the body works as a physiological machine, with all the repercussions of that knowledge on medicine, and finally to the discovery of the material basis of heredity, and its basis in DNA and the genetic code. But still, powerful though this approach is, it has so far really only been successful in connection with some of the questions we want to ask about living things, not all of them. It has given us little understanding of embryonic development; little except some rather empty theories about evolution; and hardly anything at all about the mind.

In search of a point of view which will be successful in these fields also, very few scientists, if any, are today tempted to go back to the vitalist view which was in terms of some special 'life force'. Instead one of the earliest groups who tried to think out a new point of view – mainly British biologists in the thirties (e.g. Needham, Woodger) argued that one should think of living systems as made up of the physico-chemical entities, *plus* what they called 'organizing relations' between them. These organizing relations were thought of as complicated networks of interactions, comparable to what would nowadays be called cybernetic relations (see Chapters 6 and 7), although that word had not been invented at the time. In the last thirty or forty years, there has indeed been progress in understanding the nature of the networks of interaction which are involved in the processes by which a collection of cells becomes organized into an organ with a unitary character, or into a neural system capable of functioning in a coherent way. As a development of this approach, some biologists spoke of a process of 'emergence' of new properties at certain 'levels of complexity'. By this they meant that when a mechanism, made up out of material physico-chemical parts, becomes complicated enough, it might exhibit a type of behaviour which did not and could not occur at all in the isolated parts. To give a crude example: when the engine, propeller, wings, fuselage, landing gear and so on are put together in the right way, the complicated set-up becomes an aircraft which can fly; but none of the parts can fly when isolated. It was hoped in this way to account for the fact that although man, at least, has self-consciousness, his ultimate constituents – if one takes them to be physico-chemical atoms and molecules – do not have anything of that kind at all.

The ideas, of the importance of organizing relations between the basic entities, and of the possibility of the emergence of novel properties in systems which are complicated enough, are nowadays probably the main rival to the 'nothing but material things COWDUNG'. However, there is another view, still a minority one, which makes an even more radical attack on the orthodoxy. It questions the basic assumption of the other views, that the foundation for our understanding of the world is a knowledge of material entities such as physico-chemical atoms, and is a return in modern form, to the Heraclitan 'process' philosophy as opposed to the Democritean 'thing' view. Perhaps the first influential exponents of an approach of this kind were Marx and Engels, in their attempt to *substitute a dialectical* materialism for the current *mechanical* materialism. They were, of course, concerned mostly with the social–economic–political arena; but Engels in particular wrote fairly extensively about the world of natural science. Perhaps because of their overwhelming interest in political struggles and confrontations, they argued that all the interactions involved in natural processes can be thought of in terms of the confrontation of antagonists – a thesis opposed by an antithesis, leading to a synthesis. Another author who, later, and with little reference to Marx and Engels, developed a similar line of thought more thoroughly, and much more in relation to the natural world as a whole and our knowledge of it, was A. N. Whitehead.

The basis of his view can be regarded as a return to what people had thought about science, as a means of understanding nature, in its very earliest days, well before the triumphs of Newtonian physics and its later developments in chemistry. It argues that the foundation of knowledge is not the atom, as chemists describe it, or whatever fundamental particles the most recent physicists are willing to admit. Instead science is based on observations, which, made in a controlled and organized way, amount to experiments. Now an observation, or an experiment, has to be observed by someone. It is 'an occasion of experience'; and involves the experiencing person as well as what is experienced. Thus phenomena like mind, or conscious perception, are included in the very foundation of knowledge. COWDUNG, of both the minority and majority kind, leaves mind out of what it calls objective reality, and then has to try to smuggle it back through some doctrine of organizing relations, emergence and the like.

For any view which emphasizes the process character of things, and the importance of the relations between them, the boundaries of each thing must appear somewhat indefinite, since nothing can exist totally for itself, with no involvement with anything else. However, classical logic, and most of the mathematics which is derived from it, is based on consideration of clearly defined entities with, as one might put it, definite hard edges. Recently, with the attention being paid to Heraclitan process ideas as against the Democritean atomistic ones, people are trying to develop a mathematics of 'fuzzy' entities; a logic, and, perhaps more down to earth, a computer-programming system, which deals with notions which cannot be precisely defined. Another similar development is to say that the state of a system, which conventionally would be represented by a point on a graph, should be represented by a point surrounded by a 'tolerance' region, and can lie anywhere within that region; then one deals not with a clear-cut geometrical space, but with a 'tolerance space'. Of course, many of our everyday statements, and the most important ones at that, do already deal with such concepts. Who would dare to offer precise definitions of any of the main words in statements like 'Love thy neighbour as thyself', or even 'apples are nicer than pears'? These new developments in mathematics are genuinely new Tools for Thought which, when developed, will make it possible to handle such matters more precisely.

There is no space here for a full discussion of the alternative thing or process points of view. However, there are two points which it seems useful to make. The first is relatively minor in importance, but is necessary information in relation to what one is likely to come across in reading recent material. The controversy between vitalism and mechanism, and the development of the minority view of the importance of organizing relations and emergence, was largely a European phenomenon during the thirties and forties. The Americans played little part in it, and on the whole even now do not understand what you mean if you speak of vitalism and mechanism. They became interested in the subject considerably later, indeed mostly not until the sixties, and they tend to use in this connection the word 'reductionism'. One might think at first sight that this would indicate the view that one should start from the observation or experiment, and attempt to reduce its complexity to terms of the simpler entities which one has already come across in physics and chemistry; which is just what the most radical anti-COWDUNG view would maintain. However, in American practice, the word is used in exactly the opposite sense to this. 'Reductionism' implies two rather different things. As a philosophy it means that the objective world consists of physico-chemical entities and explicitly describable interactions between them. This is the view that we have above designated as majority COWDUNG. Secondly, reductionism is a recipe for action: then it is the belief that if you are confronted with a complex situation, for instance a living system, your best bet to get some sort of pay-off or other is to look for the physical or chemical factors which can influence the phenomenon in question.

Treat sex as something in the field of chemistry, and you may come up with the Pill – a pretty definite agent which produces a pretty definite result. If, on the other hand, you refuse ever to treat it as anything less complex than the full content of occasions of sexual experience, you may find that it is even more complex than you thought (owing to the unconscious factors in it) and finish up feeling yourself bogged down in a bottomless morass of Freud, Jung, Reich, Laing and the rest. It is a difficult choice. Undoubtedly, the 'thing' view 'works', up to a point; the 'reductionist' approach to sexuality can fix it so that a girl doesn't produce a fertilizable ovum just when its presence is not wanted. But the presence or absence of a fertilizable egg is not the only thing of importance in a sexual experience. The experience *does* include factors which, one can recognize, Freud *et al.* are trying to talk about, however difficult they find it to do so in any meaningful way.

As an expression of personal opinion, I would say that reductionism is lousy philosophy (because science is based on experiments, not on atoms), but is a good recipe for making a quick (scientific) buck by discovering some useful practical information; but is bad again as a method for making major advances in human comprehension, such as those of Darwin, Freud, Einstein or the quantum physicists.

There are two points worth adding about Whitehead. In his later life he developed his philosophy into somewhat esoteric complexities. Few people except professional philosophers will wish to go into it. However, in the earlier stages of his thought, he coined two phrases which it is worth anyone's while to be acquainted with and to consider.

The first is the 'Bifurcation of Nature'; by which he meant the (to him mistaken) idea that it is possible to split nature into two separate parts, mind on the one hand, and matter on the other. This thesis is particularly associated with the name of Descartes, and is also known as the Cartesian dualism. Whitehead maintained, in opposition to this, that primitively we get to know about the world by a process which involves minds, which operate by means of our bodily material structures, interacting with external events. He claimed that an attempt to make a clean-cut break, between the subjective mental observer and the objective material observed, is a basic error. They are initially parts of a whole, and if one wants for some purposes to separate them, that can only be a matter of convenience that should be indulged in with great caution.

The second of his phrases worth remembering is 'Fallacy of Misplaced Concreteness'. Most conventional thought, he argues, recognizes certain derived, and essentially abstract, notions, that have been invented by man to try to make sense of the situations he comes across. Examples are physical atoms, or feelings such as anger, or social notions such as justice. Man tends to accept these notions as being concrete things, which could, as it were, be picked up and placed somewhere else. Whitehead argued that such notions are in fact always *derived* from actual occasions of human experience. The experiences are the real things; the notions are secondary and derivative. It is dangerous to forget this, and to take these secondary things as more concrete and real than they actually are. This is, of course, just another, but an illuminating way, of putting the argument against reductionism as a philosophy. If we accept that the universe contains things which are independent of our personal selves – then it is a fallacy to suppose that our present descriptions of these independent factors sum up the whole of their concrete reality, leaving nothing out. 'Atoms are real.' Okay, but what sort of atoms? All we know about them is what we have so far succeeded in finding out, by analysing our experiences, and arranging to have experiences (experiments) which look like being informative. The Fallacy of Misplaced Concreteness, in its simplest form (there are many more subtle forms), is to suppose that what we have so far discovered is the *whole* of what is contained in the reality independent of ourselves.

## B. Moral Philosophy

*Values*

Discussion of the philosophical nature of the world we live in – things or processes? – has been unfashionable both for academic philosophers and for ordinary people. Discussing the other main questions in philosophy, about values and ethics, has been in some ways even more pushed into the background in the last thirty or forty years. For most of European history, and of the history of most other parts of the world too, the character of the Good and the Right have been central issues for civilized thought, falling out of public discussion only in periods when there was such general agreement about them that argumentation seemed unnecessary. Rather suddenly, in the last half-century, people have begun acting as though such concepts either had no meaning at all, or, if they had any, this could be left in the hands of a few specialist theologians or a dwindling band of moral philosophers near the bottom of the scale of esteem and prestige in the academic world. Many of the younger generation today do not agree with this negligent dismissal of such matters, and I do not myself. The branch of philosophy which deals with morals and values requires discussion, even in a book with a methodological slant like this one; not because it provides Tools for Thought, but rather because it suggests what kind of tools are going to be required.

There are, of course, a large variety of opinions, and all we have space for here is to list them without attempting to compare their merits. The main varieties can be described as arising by combining items chosen from three pairs of alternatives:

*a* Nature consists of things;
*b* Nature consists of processes;
*p* Values are inside nature;
*q* Values are outside nature;
*x* Values stem from God;
*y* God stems from values.

For instance, one might believe that nature consists of things, and that the things are themselves valuable because God created them; this would be the combination of $a–p–x$. Or one might believe that nature consists of things, which have no value in themselves, but values exist and from this fact one can deduce the existence of God; this would be $a–q–y$. And so on. There are eight possible combinations, and nearly all of them have been believed by some people somewhere some time.

There can also be views which reject both of one or more of the pairs of alternatives. For instance, the most extreme variety of the 'reductionist' philosophy, which some people would have us believe is the basic philosophy of science, tells us that the world, including man, is nothing but a machine; everything is molecules and nothing but molecules. This is accepting $a$, but it is rejecting that there really are such things as values, and is thus turning down both $p$ and $q$, and $x$ and $y$. A milder form of this, which is the form originally presented by the earlier philosophers of science, such as Descartes, did at least officially accept the existence of God, and that values are derived from Him; that is to say it was the view $a–q–x$.

Perhaps, as a word of guidance (or warning) about the rest of this book, I should say that my own personal view falls under the heading $b–p–y$; nature is made up of processes, and the processes involve values, and God – if one wishes to use that term – arises from the values inherent in the processes.

*Thinking and Feeling*

In the last few years there has been a considerable revival of interest in the mode of dealing with a world which rejects the whole idea of an intellectual analysis. The only type of intellect it values is what Roszak calls 'Rhapsodic Intellect'. In effect it does not want to have anything to do with any of the alternatives listed above. It presents the feeling that intellectual thought can never be more than an exploration of relations between abstract concepts; and an abstract concept is by its very definition only a partial and incomplete reflection of reality. One of the greatest spokesmen for this point of view in classical English literature was William Blake ('to generalise is to be an idiot'). Wordsworth and the other poets of the Romantic movement of the early nineteenth century put the same point of view in a slightly less extreme form; then, more recently, D. H. Lawrence. Today it is most forcefully expressed by a group of young American writers, such as Charles Reich, Philip Slater and Theodore Roszak. These recent writers are explicitly writing *against* something which they take to be characteristic of the dominant culture – the COWDUNG of the present time. They argue that the affairs of the world are at present run solely under the influence of the *head*, whose mode of behaviour is in terms of conceptual thought; while they call for dealing with the world through the *body*, whose mode of behaviour is through spontaneous feeling and action. They usually also identify the *head* and its conceptual thinking with science, and they therefore appear as anti-scientists.

This has been an influential set of values in recent years, particularly amongst young people. In many ways quite rightly so, at least in as far as it stresses the importance of other faculties to that of conceptual thought alone. But it is actually quite wrong in its identification of science with conceptual thought, as I shall point out later when discussing the scientific methods (p. 117). Science involves thinking but does not arise from it; the groundwork of science is observation and experiment. The general exploration of our surroundings involved in asking 'what sort of things are we coming across?' brings the scientist up against just the raw material of experience which the anti-rationalists are emphasizing. Of course, science then goes on to utilize conceptual analysis, to clarify experiences and try to make sense of them. But it is basically wrong to suppose that science does not include this mode of behaviour – although it must be admitted that some scientists have tried to give that impression.

Again, I would argue that it is incorrect of the anti-scientists to attribute the present ills of the world to science as such. They arise much more from the misapplication of science under the influence of a basically inadequate social philosophy, which puts too much stress – both in capitalist and in Communist countries – on material goods. This last point, of course, goes well beyond the field of methodologies which are being discussed in this book.

*Christianity and Environment*

Another topical discussion about the importance of moral philosophy in the world today centres round the argument that it is because of the values enshrined in Western man's religion of Christianity, that he has allowed himself to ravage the natural resources of the planet and pollute his environment with his waste products. It is claimed that the sanction for these malpractices is found in the Book of Genesis, where the story of the Creation tells that God gave the earth and the plants and animals in it to the dominion of Adam for him to use as he saw fit. Exponents of this argument usually do not go on to point out that what was given to Adam at the time of the creation was the Garden of Eden, in which man, although the most important of living creatures, lived at peace with all the others. It was only after the Fall of man and the expulsion from the earthly paradise that any question of exploitation of the world by man arose.

In any case, it seems very difficult to sustain the argument that Christian man has always altered the natural ecosystems more drastically than those of other religions, or that the alterations that he has produced have always been deleterious. All great civilizations, at all times and with all manner of religions, have made profound changes in natural ecology. The Mesopotamian, Egyptian and Chinese civilizations all depended on draining swampy land and controlling the water with elaborate canals. Pretty vigorous remodellings of the landscape were necessary to support the mountain civilizations of the Incas of Peru, or the rice cultivators in the hill countries of South-East Asia, or again the great civilizations which conquered the rainless plains of Ceylon by controlling the water from the mountains. None of these, of course, were Christian. Their justification for imposing their will on the natural landscape cannot be looked for in the Book of Genesis. Moreover, some of them produced in the long run effects even more devastating than anything brought about so far by Western Christianity. Mesopotamian civilizations eventually ruined the fertility of their land and reduced the country to desert, by agricultural practices which led to the fertile soil being swept into rivers. The pre-Christian Mediterranean civilizations of Greece and Rome, combined with the Muslim civilizations in the early centuries of our era, succeeded in devastating the southern shores of the Mediterranean, which had been the granary of Rome. Moreover, on the other side of the picture, Christian civilizations cannot be accused of always wrecking their ecosystems. Christian Europe not only converted the ill-drained tangled forests north of the Alps into fertile agricultural land, but found ways of cultivating this which have kept it in good shape for about a thousand years.

The real blame for the harmful effects which man is now undoubtedly producing in industrialized Christian Western Europe and North America, can, I think, be blamed much more on the industrial components in his culture than on the Christian. Really harmful pollution – other than that caused by the age-old problem of getting rid of human excreta from large cities, which has been more satisfactorily solved in the industrial countries than in any previous civilization – began to arise with the development of heavy industry in Britain during the early phases of the Industrial Revolution. It was due almost entirely to a mixture of ignorance and lack of foresight. People simply did not know how harmful some products, such as sulphur dioxide, or heavy metals like mercury, lead and so on, could be. And they did not foresee the enormous expansion of industry which would convert a few isolated square miles of polluted region around particular industrial towns into a condition blanketing a large proportion of the country.

These lessons were not learnt until the damage had become quite considerable. However, anti-pollution laws came into operation in Britain at a relatively early stage. It was in America (followed by non-Christian Japan) that pollution rose to really spectacular levels in certain places, and it is in America that the anti-pollution outcry has therefore been most violent. The intensity of pollution in America and the feebleness of any attempt to control it until the last few years is not, I think, fairly attributable to the Puritan ethic. In the early times in American history, when the Puritan ethic was an important force in their social behaviour, the New Englanders, guided by this morality, were not particularly bad polluters; nor were the Southern cotton-growing slave-owners. Really irresponsible exploitation and pollution of nature got under way with the great influx of immigrants from the mid-nineteenth century onwards. Their behaviour was very little influenced by a Christian morality, Puritan or otherwise. It was dominated much more by the worship of the great god Molock – the dollar. There was oil, gold, copper and who knows what else to be found just beyond the western horizon. The man who got there first could take them out as fast as possible, and go on to the next piece of treasure trove, leaving behind him what mess he pleased, to be cleared up by anyone unenterprising enough to be content to try to get a second, poorer crop. It is only to shirk the real issue to attribute responsibility to these malpractices either to Christianity, or for that matter to science. They are the responsibility of unmitigated materialism – and you don't seem to make it all that much better, in this connection, by being dialectical about it.

# 2  Complexity

## A. The Nature of Complexity

*Relations, Instructions and the Mind*

This book is about the problems involved in trying to get a grasp on complexity. The following chapters will describe a number of different ways which make it not too difficult to begin to get some sort of understanding of complex systems. But some people may feel that one ought to start by defining what we shall be discussing. However, no one has yet succeeded in giving a definition of 'complexity' which is meaningful enough to enable one to measure exactly how complex a given system is. Obviously it is something to do with the number of elements which can be separately identified in the system, and with the number of ways in which they are related; but it is often a matter of choice how many elements one wishes to distinguish, and how far one wants to follow up the ramifications of their relationships and interconnections.

It is worth pointing out, though, that however one might try to define complexity, it tends to increase faster than the number of elements involved. Consider a very simple case: a number of people, all of whom get to know each other in pairs – and we will not pursue their inter-relations beyond the pairwise. If there are two people, there are two pairwise relations – $a$'s relation with $b$, and $b$'s relation with $a$, which may not be quite the same. If there are ten people each individual has nine others to know, so there are $10 \times 9 = 90$ relations; if there are fifty people, there are $50 \times 49 = 2,450$ relations and so on (Fig. 2a.1).

Roughly speaking, the relations of this sort go up as the square of the number of elements in a system. This means, for instance, that the difficulty of running something like a telephone exchange increases not in proportion to the number of subscribers, but more nearly in proportion to the square of the number – hence the installation of electronic switching apparatus in place of the village postmistress.

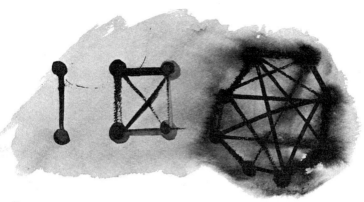

FIG. 2a.1

Something of the same sort happens with the interference with your driving by other cars on the roads, or even more generally, with the advantages and disadvantages of living in a place of high population density. Two's company, three's a crowd and five or six is getting to be a shambles.

The increase in the complexity of relations when there is an increase in the number of things to be related may seem alarming enough, but it is slight in comparison with what happens when we consider, not relations between things, but combinations of instructions. There are only a very small number of rules for moves which can be made in chess, but the number of different positions of the pieces on the board which can result when these few rules are implemented alternately by two players is truly immense. Even when there is only one 'player', and a set of rules which itself specifies which rule is to be operated at the next move, the results which are generated may be of incalculable complexity (though sometimes they can also be very simple); some examples of this are described in Chapter 9, which deals with instructions (see pp. 145–160). In such circumstances there seems to be no general definition of complexity which would be meaningful. It makes more sense to give special definitions of what one means in any particular context, to make clear what one is talking about at the time.

There is, however, one general point to bear in mind. Man's attempts to deal with complex situations have to be carried out within the limitations set by the capacities of his brain. These limitations are rather severe. Even in well-trained people, the human nervous system can process information only at the rate of 250–1,000 words per minute (in comparison, electronic equipment, using such methods as microfilm, can store and retrieve up to 700,000 words per minute; and this rate is being rapidly increased). If one considers man's capacity of considering items simultaneously, the number he can deal with is tiny. For instance, if he is subjected to a number of incoming stimuli to his various sense organs, in general he can discriminate and recognize only about seven or eight at once. Again, this is about the number of items that a man can simultaneously bring to mind, out of all those stored in his memory, and take into consideration at one and the same time when coming to a decision about something. This is a remarkably small 'channel capacity', to use the electrical engineers' term.

The seven or eight ideas that can be brought into immediate consciousness need not be items of specific detailed information. Some of them may be complex ideas or theories synthesizing into a single concept a mass of minute details. The process of formulating theoretical concepts (such as atom, gene, Oedipus complex, Hamlet and the like) is the only device that man has at his disposal to help him deal with the highly complex world. This is the essential justification for the pursuit of pure science, high-brow literature and art. Without the assistance of the symbolic concepts formulated by these apparently luxury activities, man would be reduced either to taking decisions in the light only of seven or eight particular facts, or to turning the whole thing over to a computer (which, of course, he would have had to programme without the aid of appropriate general concepts).

## B. Complexity of Information in the Modern World

It is impossible to give anything like a complete or accurate picture of the complexity of the modern world, which man has to try to handle with these somewhat imperfect instruments. However, one can get some idea of at least part of the problem by considering studies which have been made of the growth of scientific information in the last two centuries. Even this can be estimated only indirectly, by figures which give indications of trends rather than anything more precise. One such indication is the number of scientific journals published. The first two journals devoted wholly to science – *The Philosophical Transactions of the Royal Society of London*, and the French *Journal des Scavants* – were both started in 1665. A number more were begun at regular intervals during the next century. The process really got under way in earnest around 1760; and since then the number of new journals established has doubled every fifteen years (or increased ten-fold every fifty years). By now well over 100,000 scientific journals have been founded. Not all have persisted, and nobody knows quite how many journals are being published at the present time. As long ago as 1938, Bernal estimated that there were some 33,000 current scientific publications. Another estimate in the late 1960s put the number at 50,000, containing about 1 million separate scientific papers per year.

One attempt to handle this mass of material has been the foundation of secondary journals, whose function is to summarize and abstract the papers published in the primary journals. The first of these appeared as long ago as 1714 in Germany. By the time there were enough of them to form a representative sample, they also started to multiply, at the same exponential rate as the primary journals, doubling in number every fifteen years, and reaching a total of 1,900 by the mid 1960s. By this time there had been developed a tertiary level of periodical publications, giving information about the abstracting journals. At present there is a plan for a World Science Information System, under the auspices of the United Nations (UNISIST), which contemplates central computer storage of all scientific information, with a suitably elaborate retrieval system.

It is very obvious that no single man can 'know' all of this information, or even have very ready access to it; but he may be able to find any particular item, if he searches hard enough for it. The consequence of this may be that it becomes easier to rediscover a fact rather than to find out whether somebody else has already discovered and described it. One gets the impression that in some branches of science, such as parts of biology which are still floundering about in search of firm theoretical framework, a good deal of current research is already of this kind: an earnest young worker coming up with what seems to him a novel discovery, which in fact was well known about fifty years previously, although forgotten or neglected in the interim. This 'rediscovery phenomenon' may well become one of the major factors limiting the rate of advance of science.

Another effect of the mass of scientific information is that it encourages specialization. There is no evidence that the man of today can remember, and have at his fingertips, many more items than could his predecessor two centuries ago, when 1,000 fewer journals were being published. He has perforce to narrow the range of topics on which he is well informed, though not necessarily by a factor of 1,000, since, as we saw before, the development of theoretical insight makes it possible to sum up large masses of information under the heading of a single concept. Nevertheless, the narrowing of range must be quite considerable.

Attempts to overcome this difficulty by inter-disciplinary or trans-disciplinary teaching can only be successful up to a point. If, as seems to be necessary, one assumes that roughly speaking the amount that any one person can know is approximately fixed, there is no use thinking that by teaching a student two or three subjects one can get him to know as much about these subjects as do specialists who study only one of them. The purpose of inter-disciplinary teaching is best considered as the production of a different mix of interests which seems particularly relevant to important problems of the time, rather than the impossible task of adding one existing specialism to another.

One of the most important effects of the rapid increase in the volume of information is that information is very rapidly rendered obsolete by the discovery of new facts. De Solla Price has discussed this in terms of 'a coefficient of immediacy'. This is the ratio of the increase in a variable (such as information) over a period, to its value at the end of that period. For instance, if the amount of information doubles in fifteen years, it would be A at the beginning of that period and 2A at the end of it. The increase in A and the coefficient of immediacy is $\frac{A}{2A} = \frac{1}{2}$. That is to say, that at the end of the fifteen years, 50 per cent of the available information will have been discovered during that period itself.

There is another, perhaps less flattering, way of looking at this situation, which is very relevant to people who are undergoing courses of formal education. Suppose somebody's schooling finished in the year the fifteen-year period mentioned above began, then fifteen years later 50 per cent of the available information would not have been in existence when he ceased his courses of study. Unless he had gone on learning in the mean time, he could be regarded as 50 per cent obsolescent. Over a working life of forty-five years, a person in this situation would become 87·5 per cent obsolescent. In some very rapidly advancing fields, such as computer science, the doubling period is not fifteen years, but more like four years, and in such circumstances obsolescence reaches 98 per cent in only twenty-four years.

These are theoretical figures, but there is some actual evidence about the rate at which university instruction goes out of date in certain fields. A study has been made by Zelikoff (1968) of some 7,000 undergraduate and graduate courses in engineering sciences given at five major

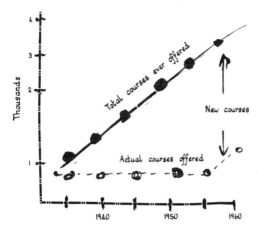

FIG. 2b.1

American universities. He took the number of courses offered at the start of a given period as representing the 'amount' of information available at that time. The quantity of 'new knowledge' accumulated during the period was estimated by the number of new courses which were offered.

From these figures, he could calculate the rate at which a person who graduated in a given year would become obsolescent if he ceased learning in the year he left college. The figures are pretty alarming to anyone

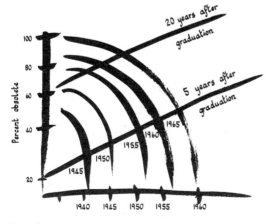

FIG. 2b.2

who thinks all you have to do is to learn a certain number of facts at university and they will last you the rest of your life. Even people who graduated in 1955 (the last year in which there was anything like sufficient factual evidence) would be about 30 per cent obsolescent five years after graduation, and nearly 60 per cent after fifteen. If one extrapolates the figures to the present time, engineers who ceased learning anything in 1970 would be getting 50 per cent out of date in as little as five years.

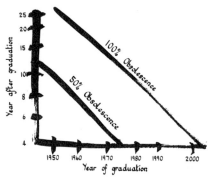

This method is, of course, only a very rought way of estimating the rate at which new knowledge is being added to the old stock, and the figures of rates of obsolescence should clearly not be taken as accurate. They are theoretical and indicative only; but they are probably right enough as orders of magnitude, and in suggesting that it only takes a few years for a considerable fraction of most people's store of knowledge to get out of date. Perhaps this is especially so in science, in which information is very actively sought, and is recorded for other people to use. But even in less formalized intellectual fields, such as the understanding of peoples, societies and political systems, the same sort of obsolescence of points of view, opinions and understanding also occurs, though possibly at a slower rate.

It would be optimistic to think that anyone really knows how to deal with the situation. The solution lies presumably in some mix of (a) teaching general principles which will go out of date only slowly, and (b) teaching methods for finding out rapidly and fairly comprehensively the up-to-date factual information which will put flesh on these bare bones at any time when it becomes necessary to apply the (c) teaching methods of classifying information into a hierarchy of categories, so that the items relevant to a particular context can be rapidly filtered out, and (d) instilling motivation for continuing self-education after the period of formal education has ceased. But exactly what this mix should be and how to achieve these ends still remains to be worked out (and should be the subject of much more vigorous debate than it usually is).

# 3   Complex Shapes

Perhaps the simplest examples of complex things which one comes across are complex shapes; in them, nothing is changing, and nothing is engaged in active interaction with anything else. Even so, they are quite difficult to grasp or describe.

## A. Symmetry and Ordered Shapes

One of the first steps we commonly take to try to make sense of a shape is to look for symmetry in it. The derivation of the word symmetry – from two Greek words meaning 'with, or accompanying' and 'measure' – gives it the very general meaning of referring to parts with similar geometrical properties; and, of course, many of the things we come across do have parts with similar properties. Human beings have a right side which is very similar to their left side; cats and dogs have four very similar legs, insects have six, spiders eight and centipedes many; and the legs are not only very similar but are arranged in an orderly way. It is an orderliness in the arrangement of similar parts which is usually meant by the word symmetry. There is no doubt that a shape which we can describe as an orderly symmetrical arrangement of similar parts is much more comprehensible and graspable by the mind than it would be if it does not contain any similar sub-parts, or if those parts were just scattered higgledy-piggledy, without any rational principles of arrangement.

However, the degree to which one can understand a complex system by finding and describing a symmetry of its shapes is really very limited. It turns out that there are only a few ways in which symmetry can be produced, and this means there are relatively few possible types of symmetry. Consider first how one could produce symmetry. Start with a single asymmetrical shape, such as a hook drawn on a sheet of paper, which bends, say, to the right. There are basically three ways in which we can arrange other hooks in some sort of symmetrical relation to it.

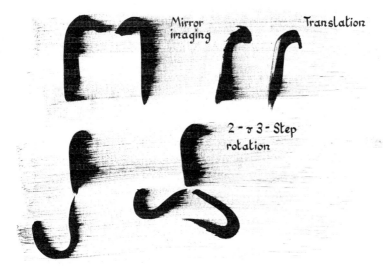

Mirror imaging

Translation

2 - π 3 - Step rotation

FIG. 3a.1

One is to produce its mirror image; if the hook is reflected in a mirror set at right angles to the plane of the paper, a new hook will be produced, this time bending to the left. Another way of producing symmetry is to imagine that there is a line perpendicular to the plane of the paper, and that the hook is rotated around this as an axis. If the revolution goes the whole way round, 360°, it of course returns to where it was before, but if the whole turn is completed in two steps, the first half-turn of 180° would produce another hook. And one could also produce symmetrical arrangements by making the whole turn in three, four, five or six steps. All the hooks produced will, of course be right-hand hooks like the original one; but one can combine these rotational symmetries with mirror symmetries, and so obtain arrangements containing both right- and left-hand hooks. There is a third way of producing symmetry, simply by displacing the original hook, through a certain distance, without either rotating or mirroring it. These three types of change determine the only three basic types of symmetry there are – reflectional, rotational and translational.

There are also only a relatively small number of ways in which these symmetries can be combined with one another. If one is concerned with flat patterns, which can be drawn on a plain sheet of paper, there are only seventeen possible arrangements of combined symmetries that will produce a pattern that does not have empty gaps in it. For instance,

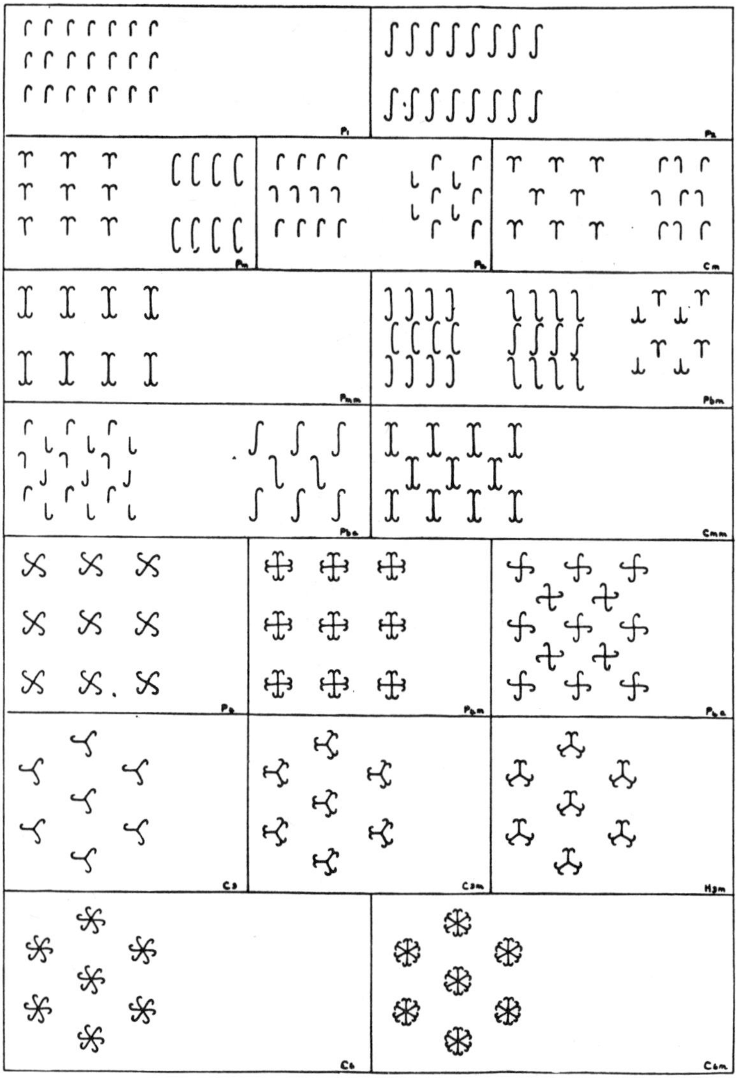

Diagram of 17 symmetry groups

Fig. 3a.2

FIG. 3a.3

pentagons produced by five-step rotations cannot be packed together without gaps, though hexagons can. The *proof* that there are only seventeen possible arrangements is quite difficult and will not be given here, but the drawing 3a.2 shows them all.

The most perfect examples of symmetry one comes across in the real world are the arrangements of atoms and molecules in crystals. These cannot, of course, be seen with the naked eye or even with an ordinary microscope; but the positions and arrangements of the atoms can be discovered by the use of X-rays. Since they are arranged in solid three-dimensional structures there are more possibilities of symmetry than there are in the two dimensions of a plane. There are in fact exactly 230, but there is little point in anyone but a chemist or crystallographer working his way through the whole list. In most of the more ordinary

F IG. 3a.4

affairs of life one is much more likely to come across things which show
only some partial degree of symmetry, rather than following completely
any of the precisely specified patterns. In many cultures artists have
used pattern symmetry as a method for introducing a certain definite
but not overwhelming sense of order into their productions.

However, symmetry, in the strict sense in which we have been using
the word here, is certainly not the only property which can impart a
degree of visual unity to a shape. There are other arrangements, in
which the parts are related in some specific mathematical ways, which
the mind can accept as orderly, even when it cannot immediately
express the precise arrangement underlining the order. For instance, a
recent artist, Max Bill, has made many explorations of two arrangements which most people find to have a strong apparent order. One is

based on the arithmetical fact that $1 + 2 + 3 + 4 + 5 + 6 + 7 + 8$ add up to thirty-six. Bill takes a square with each side six units in length and divides it into thirty-six small squares; in these he arranges different tones or colours, each characterizing one of the series of 1, 2, 3, 4, 5, 6, 7, 8. Each group is symmetrically arranged, but the whole arrangement of them within the thirty-six squares is not symmetrical in any strict form of sense, and yet is very orderly.

## B. Shapes, neither Symmetrical nor Ordered

Many, probably most, natural complex shapes exhibit little symmetry. How can they be dealt with? The conventional procedure is to think of them in terms of their outline (let us confine ourselves to two-dimensional flat shapes, for the sake of simplicity). But this is not very satisfactory. The outline is probably very difficult to describe; moreover, if we are dealing with a living thing such as a fish, worm or tadpole, the outline will change drastically as the animal wriggles, yet clearly in the same sense the shape remains the same or almost the same. Finally, if one thinks only of the outline, can we even say just where the shape is located?

Another way of treating complex shapes, developed by Harry Blum, considers the shape as made up of a number of overlapping circles, the largest that can be fitted into the shape. The centres of these circles will lie on a line or a set of lines. Such a line is known as the 'medial axis' or 'symmetry axis', since it expresses a property of the shape related to a very generalized concept of symmetry. This is illustrated below with respect to a shape taken from a painted relief by Arp (3b.1).

FIG. 3b.1

Now we can say that the location of the shape is given by the position of the centre of the largest inscribed circle. And we can alter the shape slightly, while retaining its basic form, by flexing the symmetry axis while retaining the same set of circular disks (3b.2).

Fig. 3b.2

To describe a shape in these terms, one has to know not only the symmetry axis, but also the size of the circles which are to be centred on it (3b.3).

Fig. 3b.3

One of the simplest ways to provide this information is to regard the circles as bases of cones with some standard angle of slope (3b.4). Then the apices of these cones will lie on a line in the three-dimensional space above the shape, and the height of any particular apex will be precisely

Fig. 3b.4

44

related to the radius of the circle from which it arises. The whole shape is then described by this one 'ridge line' in three-dimensional space.

The symmetry-axis description can be used very conveniently in connection with some sorts of growth processes. All we need to do is to give rules for the way the sizes of the various circles, or the times at which they are initiated, change as time passes. For instance, in 3b.5 we have assumed a branched symmetry axis, with circles being initiated at a constant rate from the top downwards, and, when initiated, growing out at a constant speed; the 'contour lines' give the outline of the resulting shape at successive intervals of time. This way of representing the result is sometimes spoken of as a 'grass-fire': it is what would happen if one started a fire in a field of dry grass, which spread faster along the symmetry axis and more slowly outwards until it met some other already burnt area.

FIG. 3b.5

The drawings in 3b.6 show successive stages of a system in which the circles are all initiated at the same time, but grow faster near the lower end of the axis, while the axis itself becomes curved more rapidly at the other, slow-growing end. Clearly there are a great many changing and growing shapes which can be described in this manner.

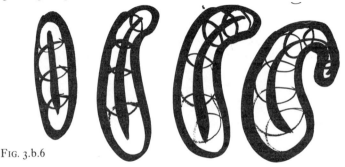

FIG. 3.b.6

The strengths and weaknesses of methods like this can only be appreciated when one tries to use them. Here is an example in which Blum's method has been found useful. People who try to reconstruct the evolution of man from his ape-like ancestors have to work from the comparatively few rare fossils of the intermediate forms – the 'missing links' – that have so far been turned up. Some of these bones, including some of the most important of them, have complex shapes which are difficult to grasp. There is, for instance, a famous bone which was found at Sterkfontein in South Africa, and is clearly part of the pelvis of some creature which bears resemblances both to the great apes and to the human species. It is a puzzling sort of shape to get a hold of. In fact although many bones in the body have been given technical names, based on recognizable forms which they suggest, this bone is technically known as 'the innominate', that is to say the unnamed, presumably because it does not really suggest anything in particular. However, it is one of the parts of the skeleton that has to get modified during the evolution from running on all fours to walking upright, and its changes in shape are therefore very important in connection with the evolution of the upright position of man.

There has always been considerable controversy among students of these matters, whether it really shows more resemblance to the similar bone in the apes or in the humas. One can see their difficulties by looking at the drawings in 3b.7 and 3b.8 which show, from two different points of view, the innominate bones of the chimpanzee, modern man, a modern pygmy of small stature and the Sterkfontein fossil. Most comparisons that have been made have involved extremely elaborate measurements of the outlines, and complicated statistical analyses, resulting in tables of figures which are not very easy to grasp. However, Charles Oxnard has applied the Blum technique of 'medial axis transformation', by which the shape of the complex outline is transformed into somewhat simpler shapes of internal medial lines. This makes it easy to see that from some points of view, for instance that from which it was drawn in 3b.7, the fossil has strong resemblances to the human; while from another point of view, such as that used in 3b.8, it is much less like the human and more like the chimpanzee. Thus the method makes it fairly easy to visualize the broad outlines of the resemblances and differences between these forms. It does not, however, easily result in numerical or quantitative estimates of resemblance. Moreover, it is undoubtedly a weakness that the analysis has to be made on a series of two-dimensional outlines, whereas really, of course, one is trying to compare three-dimensional solid structures. However, it is always difficult, except for a few exceptional people, to visualize solid structures very clearly, and most people have to be content with seeing what three-dimensional shapes look like in two-dimensional projections, as we have done here.

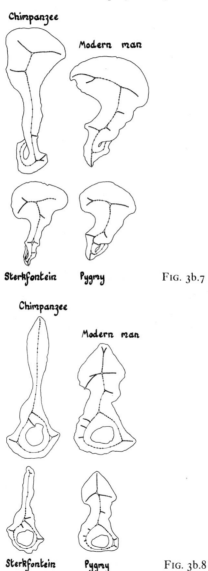

FIG. 3b.7

FIG. 3b.8

# 4   The Structure of Complex Systems

A shape, however complex, can only be a description of an appearance; but to begin to understand a thing or a system, we have to find out about its structure. This will be the subject of this chapter; in later ones we shall go on to discuss the changes and operations of structures.

Perhaps the simplest kind of structure a complex system can have is a hierarchical chain of command, such as one finds in an army with its general at the top, its battalion commanders, company commanders, platoon commanders and so on down to the common soldier. If one makes a diagram with a dot for each individual, then they can be arranged in a tree-like order, corresponding to the chain of command and responsibility.

This is, of course, a very simple type of organized structure, and when we are dealing with an organization of human relationships based on this principle it is usually quite easy to discover which level of the hierarchy any person belongs to. But he may belong to different levels in different hierarchies. Someone who is a private soldier in an army may at the same time be a member of Parliament, or a priest in an organized church, and therefore occupy much higher levels in those hierarchies.

## A. Hierarchies

The concept of a hierarchy is a very basic one in considering the organization of a complex entity. We are so used to it that when we find ourselves in a social set-up which we don't understand our first tendency is to ask 'who is boss around here?' And when we try to organize a social system of some other kind, perhaps more democratic and more pluralistic, there is often a great tendency for it gradually to turn itself into a hierarchical system of the traditional kind in which a few people boss the rest.

It is a principle of organization which has been found very convenient

48

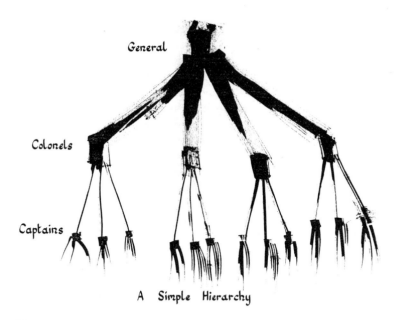

General

Colonels

Captains

A Simple Hierarchy

FIG. 4a.1

in dealing with many organized systems apart from those involved in man's social life. For instance in biology it is convenient, in fact probably essential, to distinguish between different levels of operation which can be considered as levels in a hierarchical system; for instance, the ecological level, which includes all the living things and the natural resources available in a certain region; the level of the individual animal, e.g. a rabbit; the level of its organs, its liver, kidneys and so on; the cellular level; and then several different sub-cellular levels.

The still only partially solved problem is: when is one tempted, or when is it justified, to analyse a complicated system into a hierarchical structure involving different levels? The best answer that seems to be available is that we do this when, having analysed the complex into a number of more elementary units, we look at the relationships of these units and find that the inter-relations fall into a few separate classes with few intermediates. For instance, there may be a number of quite strong interactions and a number of weaker ones, but few in between; or the activities going on in the system may be classified into very fast ones and very slow ones, again with few intermediates. If you found yourself confronted with an army with a strange uniform, whose insignia of rank you did not understand, you would find, if you were allowed to observe things, that there was some individual who would spend five minutes deciding that B company would advance along that road, accompanied by X battery of artillery; and B company and X battery would spend the next couple of hours trying to do so; while this person had gone on in the next five minutes to say that a squadron of fighter bombers would carry out a raid lasting for four hours on some other target and, long before they had done that, would order the tanks to do something else. He would be acting on a time scale much faster than that of the people he was interacting with. This would be good grounds for saying that he was higher up on the hierarchy, at a level above, capable of and empowered to give orders to and delegate responsibilities to, the people at the levels below.

The different classes of interactions need not always be connected with time scale. If you look at all the cells in the body of an animal, you find that they fall into groups with strong interactions between those in the same group (for instance all the kidney cells in the kidney, or all the liver cells in the liver), and much less interaction, though still some, between the kidney and the liver cells. You could then say that the cells were arranged in a hierarchical organization, with organs such as kidney and liver forming a higher level, and the cells grouped under these various organs making up the level below. If one wants to ask, for instance, is a city a hierarchical organization?, one would have to look to see if one could detect important activities and interactions which fall into contrasting groups of intensity or time constants (I doubt if one would find many; I do not think that cities are hierarchically organized in their activities, though they may often be in their administrative apparatus).

It is essential to remember that hierarchies, in the sense they have been discussed here, are only descriptions of structure; they do not imply that 'lower levels' in the hierarchy are 'lower' in all the possible senses of that word. For instance, it is clear that some special functions may be delegated to members of a fairly low level in the hierarchy (e.g. to a colonel or a captain in an army), and he may then have full responsibility for that particular task. Again, members of a low level (e.g. dustmen or workers in a sewage plant) may carry out functions on which all the higher levels are quite dependent. The whole subject of how a hierarchically organized human association works – what is its strategy, what its tactics, and who gives orders about what? – is one of the major preoccupations of the important subject of Management Science.

Simon has brought out one of the reasons why organization into a hierarchy is both so useful and so usual; he puts it in a parable about two watch-makers, Hora and Tempus, both of whom produced very fine, accurate watches. But Hora had designed his on a hierarchical scheme; he could put together ten components into a stable sub-assembly, which he could leave aside for a time; then he could put together ten different sub-assemblies into a major part; and finally ten major parts into the whole watch. Tempus hadn't planned it that way. His watch had a thousand parts, just as Hora's did. But he had to get them assembled all at one time; if he had got only half of them put together, but then had to stop work for a bit, they rapidly fell apart. And, of course, producing such good watches, they were both very often called on by customers, and had to stop what they were doing at the moment, to serve them or take orders. So Hora found the interruptions a bit of a nuisance, but they never set him back more than a ten-stage operation; but poor Tempus found it practically impossible to complete a watch at all; he might have got it to stage 950, when the telephone or the doorbell rang, and by the time he could get the customer out of his hair without losing his custom, the watch might have fallen apart down to stage 250 or even worse.

This is, of course, no more than the rationale on which Henry Ford I made his fortune, and saddled the modern world with the materially enriching but humanly brutalizing hierarchically organized assembly lines of mass production. It is a method that works; but its price is a bit stiffer than you might guess at first sight. But hierarchical organization has, in fact, been adopted by an extraordinarily wide range of *natural* systems.


## B. Other Types of Order

There are many types of organization in which the component elementary units are not related to one another in a strictly hierarchical order, but in some more complicated way. The structure cannot be represented by a simple hierarchical tree diagram as in the drawing 4a.1; but, as we shall see, one can often show it as a somewhat modified tree. There are also other ways of making diagrams of these structures which look rather odd at first sight to older people, although young children are now often taught about them in elementary schools which teach the 'New Maths'.

It will be well to begin by considering an organized structure which is not changing; neither the structure as a whole, nor its component parts, alter as time passes; but the units have certain relations with each other, and we want to express these in a way which makes it easy to get a general grasp of how the whole thing is put together. Take as an example an organized complex made up of five elementary units, $a$, $b$, $c$, $d$ and $e$, which may be anything from, say, individual people who are related by bonds of friendship at various degrees of intimacy, or towns at various distances from each other, all the way up to such complex factors as population, food, pollution, natural resources, capital investment, etc., whose relations with each other constitute the 'organization' of the World Problem.

Obviously we cannot say much about the structure of the organization unless we know something about the strength of the relations or the interactions between the units. Obviously also, we shall never know enough about these strengths. We shall always, or at least should always, be trying to discover more. What we are concerned with here, however, is the most convenient way of expressing whatever we do know at the present time.

The most complete way of expressing this information is to list the five components $a$, $b$, $c$, $d$ and $e$ along a horizontal line and also vertically, and at each square where say the $b$ column intercepts the $c$ row, write down some figure indicating the strength of the interaction between $b$ and $c$ (where the $b$ column meets the $b$ row, we can insert some sign indicating identity). This will give a table or 'matrix', made up of a lot of figures, like the charts of distances between towns, e.g. in the Automobile Association handbook.

|   | $a$ | $b$ | $c$ | $d$ | $e$ |
|---|---|---|---|---|---|
| $a$ | $x$ | 2·0 | 0·8 | 4·1 | 2·9 |
| $b$ | 2·0 | $x$ | 4·1 | 2·9 | 1·9 |
| $c$ | 0·8 | 4·1 | $x$ | 3·1 | 1·0 |
| $d$ | 4·1 | 2·9 | 3·1 | $x$ | 3·9 |
| $e$ | 2·9 | 1·9 | 1·0 | 3·9 | $x$ |

FIG. 4b.1

It is difficult for anyone who is not an arithmetical genius to get much sense out of it merely by inspection. One first step to making it more comprehensible is to forget about being really accurate and to group the figures into a few classes. Sometimes it is good enough to simplify really drastically, and simply say that a given pair either does interact enough to count or does not intereact enough to count. Or one might be a bit more informative, and say that it interacts strongly, or it interacts weakly, or does not interact; or one can have a still more detailed classification including identity (5), strong (4), moderate (3), weak (2) and very feeble (1) interactions. Then the table above turns into:

|   | a | b | c | d | e |
|---|---|---|---|---|---|
| a | 5 | 2 | 1 | 4 | 3 |
| b | 2 | 5 | 4 | 3 | 2 |
| c | 1 | 4 | 5 | 3 | 1 |
| d | 4 | 3 | 3 | 5 | 4 |
| e | 3 | 2 | 1 | 4 | 5 |

FIG. 4b.2

It is clear that although these simplifications may make the systems a bit easier to comprehend, it will involve making the picture less accurate. We are losing information in order to gain comprehensibility.

The next step to making the picture more easy to grasp is to rearrange things to bring out any natural groups there may be in the system. There are several ways of doing this, each with its own advantages and disadvantages, and some with more visual impact than others.

One visually appealing way is to represent the strengths of interactions by tones, or sizes of dots, instead of numbers. Thus one could turn the table above (which classifies relations in five ways) to a pattern of tones or spots like the figures 4b.3 or 4b.4. This in itself does not seem to make the picture much more easy to understand.

However, we could then try to rearrange the rows and columns in such a way as to produce a more comprehensible pattern. For instance,

FIG. 4b.3

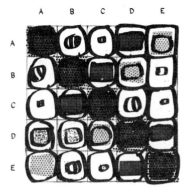

FIG. 4b.4

the rearrangement in 4b.5 or 4b.6 produces a dark area at the top left occupied by the three members, A, E, D, and another at the bottom right where there is strong interaction between the members B and C. For instance, if A, B, C, D and E were people all acquainted with each other A, E and D would be one group of specially close friends, and B and C another. The trouble about this procedure is that it is not always obvious how to rearrange the rows and columns to produce the most clear-cut patterns.

|   | A | E | D | B | C |
|---|---|---|---|---|---|
| A | 5 | 3 | 4 | 2 | 1 |
| E | 3 | 5 | 4 | 2 | 1 |
| D | 4 | 4 | 5 | 3 | 3 |
| B | 2 | 2 | 3 | 5 | 4 |
| C | 1 | 1 | 3 | 4 | 5 |

FIG. 4b.5

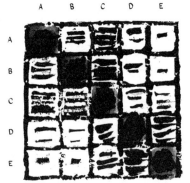

FIG. 4b.6

Another way to exhibit the relations in a visual form is to turn them into a 'tree diagram' or 'dendrogram'. This has the effect of showing the structure as a modified hierarchy, with some gaps and jumps. To do this, the five components are written in a line at the bottom and the appropriate ones are connected together at successively higher levels, indicating interactions, of strengths 4, 3, 2 and 1. Again the diagram would be simpler if one could find a suitable arrangement into which to place the elements in the lowest line. It is usually best to start by grouping together those which interact most strongly (4b.7). In this example, a and d, d and e, and b and c, all interact at strength 4. Furthermore we may notice that d interacts more strongly with b and c

54

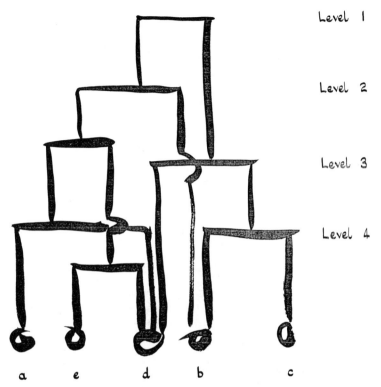

Level 1

Level 2

Level 3

Level 4

a    e    d    b    c

FIG. 4b.7

than a and e do. It is fairly simple, therefore, in this case to see that the best arrangement will be put to a, e and d in one group and b and c in another, and to have d next to b and c. Thus a good order to try will be a, e, d, b, c. Now in the line above, representing Level 4, we can connect a and d, e and d, and b and c. At the next Level, 3, we have to make a channel of communication between a and e (this in the diagram also makes another roundabout connection between e and d, but as there is already a shorter connection between them at Level 4, this does not signify). At this Level we also have to connect b and c with d. At the next Level, 2, the only new connections to make are between b and a and e. Finally at Level 1 we will have to establish a connection between c and a and e.

The way to use such a diagram is as follows: if we want to know what is the relation between b and say d, we have to discover to what Level in the tree we have to go before we find a bridge to get across from one to the other. In this case it is at Level 3. If we want to get from b to a or e we have to go up to Level 2.

Another way of drawing exactly the same information as there is in a tree diagram is to make what is called a Venn diagram. In this components are written down not in a line, but in some suitable arrangement on the page. Then outlines are drawn enclosing the ones which interact together, the heaviness of the line corresponding to the strength of the interaction. So we shall draw heavy lines around the pairs A and D, E and B, and B and C. Next we draw a thinner line round the groups which interact with strength 3 or more. This gives the two groups, A, D, E and B, C, D. Then with a still thinner line we surround A, B, D, E, which interact with strength 2 or more. And finally with a thinner line still we bring in C which includes interactions at strength 1 (4b.8).

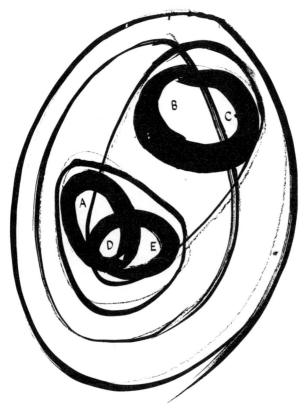

Fig. 4b.8

56

These methods of making diagrams of the relationships are useful in so far as they stimulate the imagination, and help one to get a 'feeling' for the situation which will allow one to see how to go further into it.

The diagrams are still obviously very complicated. The only way to prevent this is to leave out some more of the information in the original table. For instance, instead of using four categories to measure the strength of interaction (strong, moderate, weak and very weak), we might use only three, lumping the very weak along with the weak. We should then simplify our tree diagram and Venn diagram to 4b.9 and 4b.10.

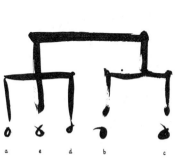

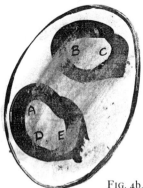

Fig. 4b.9                                                Fig. 4b.10

If we went down to only two classes (strong and weak), now lumping the moderate ones with the strong ones, we should get the figures 4b.11 or 4b.12. These are getting quite easy to understand, but unfortunately they do not tell us very much about the system in detail.

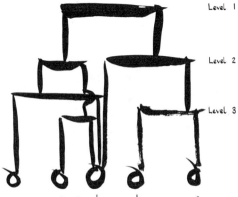

Fig. 4b.11        Fig. 4b.12

Another way of forming a mental image of the system, which is stimulating to the imagination of people who like to think of solid structures, is to regard the lines in the Venn diagram as contour lines on a map, and use them to build up a 'mountain', whose three-dimensional shape would then incorporate the information in the Venn diagram. This can be done quite straightforwardly if we have used a lot of simplification to get a tree diagram like 4b.11, and a Venn diagram on which the loops at any one level do not intercept.

a       d       e       b       c

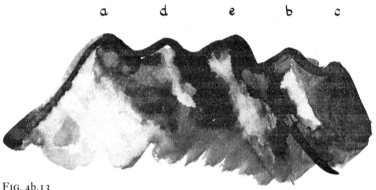

FIG. 4b.13

If we have used less simplification, and Venn loops of a given level intercept one another, we have to be content with less precision in making the mountain. With a bit of fiddling it is often possible to model a three-dimensional structure, which gives quite a good overall picture of relationships (4b.14 is an attempt to visualize 4b.10 as a mountain).

There is still another different way of giving visual form to the relationships such as those set out in the table we started with. This is to

FIG. 4b.14

write down the five elements, a, b, c, d and e on the page rather as one did for the Venn diagram, then draw lines between those which are related to one another. If we are using several grades of relationship, we can use thicker lines for strong relationships and thinner lines for weaker ones. We then get what is called an association graph, 4b.15, a methodological tool which has been much used by those planning buildings or cities.

FIG. 4b.15

It would be particularly useful if one could 'scale' such diagrams. That is to say, arrange the five points so that the distances between them are inversely proportional to the strengths of their relationships, so that the closely related ones are near together and the weakly related ones farther apart. This is just what an architect would like to do when planning a group of buildings. Another group of workers who would be very interested to develop such methods are people studying the natural grouping (species, genera, etc.) of animals and plants based on the characteristics of the organisms, rather than on their supposed evolutionary history.

Unfortunately it is not always possible to carry out an accurate scaling. For instance if you have only three elements, a, b and c, it might be that the relationship between a and b will be say 2, and between a and c, 3, but between b and c, perhaps 20. This might be so, for instance, if a was a central city, b and c suburbs and you were measuring the time of travel between them. Clearly one cannot place three points on a plane so that the distances between them are 2, 3 and 30. You cannot have a triangle unless the length of the longest side is less than the sum of the lengths of the other two sides. Sometimes one can get out of such difficulties by changing the character one is measuring. In this case the interesting relation between the city and the two suburbs might be brought out sufficiently if we measure not lengths of time of travel, but the number of trips people actually made between the three pairs of points. You would presumably find a lot between a and b, and between a and c, and quite few between b and c, and it might be possible that these figures could be plotted on to a properly scaled diagram.

Procedures for scaling, or trying to scale, sets of relations may become rather complicated. I will discuss them a little more, but I would advise those who have no sense of mathematics that they will not lose much if they skip the rest of this section.

It is not possible to scale, accurately, the association graph of the set of interactions we have been using as an example. If the points a, b, c, d, e, were to be set apart by the reciprocal of the closeness of interactions, the distance should be as in 4b.16.

|   | a | e | d | b |
|---|---|---|---|---|
| e | 4/3 |   |   |   |
| d | 1 | 1 |   |   |
| b | 2 | 2 | 4/3 |   |
| c | 4 | 4 | 4/3 | 1 |

Fig. 4b.16

It is quite easy to arrange a, d and e at the right distances apart (4b.17). Then b and c should be one unit apart, somewhere along the circle bed, which is defined by their distance from d; but then b should also be on circle ab to get the right distance from a, and also on circle eb to be right with regard to e; and it cannot be both. One would have to accept some compromise, putting b perhaps at B', a bit too near a and a bit too far from e. There are even worse difficulties about c. It should be four units away from both a and e, and this would take it right off the diagram. The best one can do is to put it as far as possible beyond the ab and eb circles, without letting it get too far away from d.

In general, however, one simply has to accept that in any complicated situation completely accurate scaling is likely to be impossible. Various methods have been worked out for estimating the degree of distortion which any given scaled diagram imposes on the actual data. There are

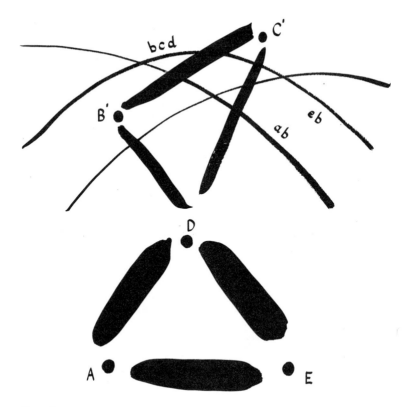

F<small>IG</small>. 4b.17

also methods for using a computer to calculate the best possible scaling that can be made from a given set of data on to, say, a flat sheet of paper, or possibly as a three-dimensional model. However, this is only for really professional purposes where a high degree of quantitative accuracy is required. Fairly rough and ready scaled association graphs prepared with nothing more elaborate than common sense and a bit of trial and error often give one quite a good mental picture of a complicated set of relationships.

To give an example I'll quote one given by Philip Tabor. This showed the relationships between twenty-one departments in a fairly large town hall, the relationships being measured by the number of trips and messages that passed between them. The actual figures are given in 4b.18. From these you can make a scaled association graph which is not too badly distorted and which comes out looking like 4b.19.

|    | 1   | 2  | 3  | 4  | 5  | 6 | 7  | 8  | 9  | 10 | 11 | 12 | 13 | 14 | 15 | 16 | 17 | 18 | 19 | 20 |
|----|-----|----|----|----|----|---|----|----|----|----|----|----|----|----|----|----|----|----|----|----|
| 2  | 176 |    |    |    |    |   |    |    |    |    |    |    |    |    |    |    |    |    |    |    |
| 3  | 0   | 1  |    |    |    |   |    |    |    |    |    |    |    |    |    |    |    |    |    |    |
| 4  | 63  | 12 | 0  |    |    |   |    |    |    |    |    |    |    |    |    |    |    |    |    |    |
| 5  | 7   | 14 | 0  | 32 |    |   |    |    |    |    |    |    |    |    |    |    |    |    |    |    |
| 6  | 8   | 3  | 0  | 2  | 1  |   |    |    |    |    |    |    |    |    |    |    |    |    |    |    |
| 7  | 10  | 13 | 0  | 42 | 13 | 0 |    |    |    |    |    |    |    |    |    |    |    |    |    |    |
| 8  | 210 | 87 | 0  | 72 | 13 | 4 | 10 |    |    |    |    |    |    |    |    |    |    |    |    |    |
| 9  | 13  | 7  | 0  | 21 | 25 | 4 | 0  | 49 |    |    |    |    |    |    |    |    |    |    |    |    |
| 10 | 0   | 17 | 15 | 0  | 0  | 0 | 0  | 0  | 0  |    |    |    |    |    |    |    |    |    |    |    |
| 11 | 3   | 1  | 0  | 0  | 0  | 0 | 0  | 0  | 0  | 0  |    |    |    |    |    |    |    |    |    |    |
| 12 | 5   | 3  | 0  | 0  | 5  | 2 | 5  | 4  | 0  | 0  | 0  |    |    |    |    |    |    |    |    |    |
| 13 | 1   | 3  | 0  | 3  | 1  | 4 | 0  | 0  | 0  | 0  | 0  | 0  |    |    |    |    |    |    |    |    |
| 14 | 11  | 2  | 0  | 0  | 0  | 1 | 0  | 0  | 0  | 0  | 0  | 0  | 0  |    |    |    |    |    |    |    |
| 15 | 6   | 12 | 0  | 0  | 0  | 1 | 2  | 6  | 1  | 0  | 0  | 0  | 0  | 2  |    |    |    |    |    |    |
| 16 | 13  | 66 | 62 | 1  | 0  | 5 | 1  | 76 | 0  | 0  | 0  | 0  | 1  | 3  | 12 |    |    |    |    |    |
| 17 | 4   | 11 | 0  | 0  | 0  | 0 | 0  | 0  | 0  | 0  | 0  | 0  | 0  | 0  | 0  | 18 | 13 |    |    |    |
| 18 | 3   | 1  | 0  | 0  | 7  | 0 | 0  | 0  | 0  | 0  | 0  | 0  | 0  | 0  | 0  | 0  | 0  | 1  |    |    |
| 19 | 0   | 2  | 0  | 0  | 0  | 0 | 0  | 0  | 20 | 0  | 0  | 0  | 0  | 0  | 0  | 0  | 0  | 0  | 0  |    |
| 20 | 24  | 39 | 3  | 4  | 24 | 2 | 0  | 0  | 0  | 0  | 10 | 0  | 0  | 0  | 0  | 10 | 0  | 0  | 6  | 0  |
| 21 | 0   | 8  | 0  | 0  | 0  | 0 | 0  | 2  | 0  | 0  | 0  | 0  | 0  | 0  | 0  | 0  | 5  | 0  | 0  | 0  |

FIG. 4b.18

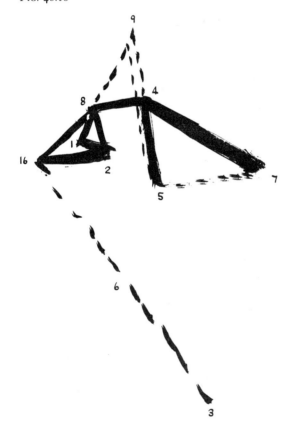

This shows clearly the particularly close relationship between 1 and 8 and 1 and 2; while between 2 and 8 it was rather less, but still quite strong (1 was the Town Clerk, 2 was the Treasurer and 8 the Estate Surveyor).

Finally, one can use such a scaled association graph as a basis for a Venn diagram if one makes a simple one with non-overlapping contours. It comes out looking like 4b.20, and that can be turned into the mountain 4b.21.

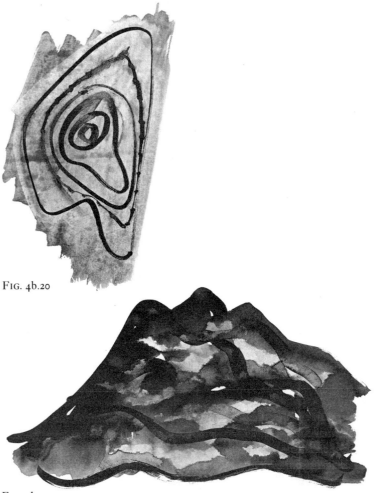

Fig. 4b.20

Fig. 4b.21

# 5   Processes in Complex Systems

We have so far been considering the structure of systems in which, although things are going on, the system itself remains the same as time passes. We now have to consider systems which alter with the lapse of time.

Time is of fundamental importance in two ways. For one thing, it is an essential part of reality. Everything real lasts some length of time, changing more, less or inappreciably, as time passes. An instantaneous moment is an abstract notion, sometimes useful but never real. As Whitehead remarked, the present is really the fringe of memory tinged with anticipation. Then, again, any attempt to influence the world has to act on the processes which are going on. Temporal change is the basic medium of all activity, including our own. For both these reasons, an understanding merely of the structure of a complex system is not enough; we must try to understand it as an inter-related set of *processes*.

## A. Open and Closed Systems

A first important distinction is between closed and open systems. A closed system, as the name implies, is one that is entirely contained within some envelope through which nothing passes either inwards or outwards. All changes go on within the bag which insulates the system from the rest of the world. In an open system, in contrast, things pass into the system from the outside, are processed, and something else is extruded outwards again.

The conventional mechanical dynamics which are usually taught in school – balls rolling down inclined planes, levers, cog-wheels, bodies colliding with each other, or billiard balls bouncing off cushions, and all the rest of 'Newtonian mechanics' – really applies to closed systems only. The great laws, of the Impossibility of Perpetual Motion, and the Second Law of Thermodynamics, that things always tend to become less well ordered, are laws of closed systems. But nearly all the systems one has to deal with in the real world are open systems, because they are really part-systems. The only completely closed system is the universe as a whole, and it is only a few astronomers who have to think seriously about that.

It is quite difficult to think of natural examples of smaller closed systems, but perhaps a barrel of wine which is gradually maturing, or a cheese which is ripening inside an airproof container, would be examples. Since any sort of change requires some energy, the closed system can only undergo change if it includes a stock of energy-yielding material which can be gradually utilized. It is the sugar in the grape juice which supplies energy for the fermentation processes in the maturing wine. Even 'Space-Ship Earth', which we are often advised to think of as a body completely isolated in space, dependent only on its stores of enclosed energy, is actually all the time receiving a very considerable supply of energy from the radiation of the sun. Animals, plants, human society, ecosystems and so on are obviously open systems, since they always receive inputs of food or other sources of energy, and raw materials of various kinds; and produce various kinds of wastes and artefacts.

## B. Growth

The word 'growth' is often applied to almost anything which increases in size with the passage of time; and we have only to admit the possibility of de-growth or negative growth to apply it also to systems which get smaller as time passes. Change of size with time is such a common phenomenon in human, social or economic affairs that it is necessary to have some notion of the ways in which it can be described. These can be most precisely and neatly expressed in mathematical language; but the basic ideas are quite simple, and can also be expressed without much difficulty in ordinary English; it will become apparent that the mathematical symbols, which at first sight scare off some people who have got into their heads the foolish notion that mathematics is too difficult for them, are really quite simple to understand.

Growing things may be of two kinds. They may be populations, whose size can be estimated by counting the number of individuals in them; for instance, people in a nation, or bacteria or other cells in a culture. What increases, then, is the total number of countable individuals. Alternatively the growing system may be a continuous mass, whose size has to be estimated by weighing it or measuring it; in this case the thing that increases is the number of units of weight or units of measurement. In discussing the basic ideas about growth there is usually no need to make this distinction explicitly. We shall refer to both these measures of the growing system as measures of its size.

The simplest form of growth is one in which the system increases by a certain amount in each unit in time. That is to say, the rate of growth is constant. If, for instance, at the beginning of the process we take the size of the system as $x_0$, then after a time $t$, its size will be $x_0 + kt$, where $k$ is the amount added in each unit time. This is what happens when a series of equal-sized drops of water fall from a leaky tap into a bucket placed below it.

In living systems growth of this sort is rather rare. Instead, the amount of new growth is usually very much dependent on the amount of the growing system which is already in existence. For instance, the number of children born in a population depends in some way (not always a very simple way) on the number of existing individuals who can act as parents. The simplest situation of this kind is one in which the rate of growth (i.e. the amount added in unit time) depends directly on the size of the system already there. This would be so if in a human population everyone got married, and each pair of parents always produced a certain number of children (say four), all of whom lived to maturity to become parents in their turn. Another example would be a fattening calf which always put on a given fraction of its existing body weight during the course of the next twenty-four hours.

*Exponential Growth*

This sort of growth is known as exponential growth. Another way of expressing it is to say that the absolute size increases exponentially. This name is derived from the mathematical expression of the situation. If the size of the system is called $x$, and the rate of increase in size is written either as $\frac{dx}{dt}$ (i.e. the difference in $x$ which occurs over a very short time $dt$) or something even more shortly as $x$. If this rate of increase is directly proportional to the size we shall have the equation $\frac{dx}{dt} = kx$, where $k$ is the constant of proportionality. From this equation it follows mathematically (though we do not need here to go into why this is so) that at any given time, $t$, the size $x = x_0 e^{kt}$ where $x_0$ is the initial size from which the system began. The word exponential refers to the fact that in this formula time, $t$, comes in as a power of the number, $e$, as 2 comes in as a power written above the line in the expression $x^2$.

This type of growth has some rather remarkable properties, which can most easily be seen by drawing a graph of the relation between size and time.

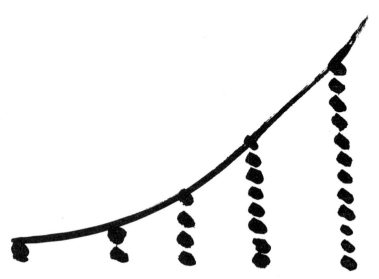

FIG. 5b.1

Drawing 5b.1 shows the growth of a simple exponential system. It starts with one unit at time $t_1$; at time $t_2$ it adds something of the same size itself, i.e. it adds 1, or doubles itself. By time $t_3$ it adds on another piece at the same size as it is, i.e. doubles itself again. Thus it grows from 1 to 2 to 4 to 8, 16, 32. The amounts added in each interval get larger as the system itself gets larger. It will be seen that the absolute size seems to be getting larger at a faster and faster rate. This is necessarily so since the rate at which it increases is proportional to the size itself, so that if that gets bigger the rate of increase must also get bigger.

One peculiar consequence of this is that, once the process has been going on for some time, the rate of increases becomes so fast that it only takes a short period for the system to add on to itself as much as everything it had contained in the past. Consider for instance a population of an annual plant in which at the end of each season each plant produces two seeds which give two plants in the following season. Starting from one plant the numbers in the population go 1, 2, 4, 8, 16,

32, 64, 128 . . . If you care to add up to the total number of plants that had ever been in existence up to and including any particular generation, say that in which there were 128 individuals, you will find that the total of the previous generations amount to 127. Thus in such a system you could always say that of all the plants there have ever been, more than half are alive at the present time. This sort of argument is often used, either to spread alarm and despondency, or alternatively in a boastful way, about situations in human populations (of all the scientists, or artists, or houses, or automobiles, or crimes of violence, etc., etc., that there have ever been, more than half happened in our lifetime). This is a simple consequence of exponential growth – if exponential growth really occurs for very long, which we shall see is very doubtful.

## Compound Interest and Discounting the Future

One of the most widely known examples of exponential growth is money put out at compound interest. You lend £100 at 6 per cent interest, and at the end of the first year you have got £106; at the end of the next year you get 6 per cent not on the £100 but on £106, and so on. A reasonably accurate formula for what will eventually happen is the 'Seventy Law'. If the rate of interest is X per cent, the sum you have invested will have doubled in 70/X years. At 10 per cent it will have doubled in seven years; at 6 per cent it will have doubled in somewhat under twelve years; and it will go on doubling again every seven or twelve years as the case may be.

This is fine if it is your own money. If you can lay down £100 and get a steady 6 per cent on it, in 100 years this will have doubled a bit over eight times and will be getting on for £26,000. A nice little nest-egg for your great-grandchildren.

It is probably more important to appreciate how the system works in reverse, as it were. Somebody starts building a factory, or undertakes some other long-term exercise, which in, say, thirty years is going to be causing pollution to which society has by that time woken up, and which it will want to control. Say it would cost £100,000 to install the extra mechanisms required to deal with the danger of pollution. If the firm building the factory is not going to be obliged legally, or by some other social pressure, to provide this purification plant until sometime about thirty years in the future, it can't possibly afford (in straight financial terms) to build it into the plant from the beginning. Thirty years hence, £100,000 will represent only about £20,000 now, at say 6 per cent compound interest; and that is clearly not nearly enough to build the required machinery. If, instead of spending the £100,000 on building the purification plant into the factory, where it won't be demanded of you for thirty years, you invested it in something else at 6 per cent, it would have doubled more than twice and be worth nearly £500,000 before you were called upon to provide the anti-pollution facility. The financial system is such that people are compelled to discount (i.e. neglect) the future, at a rate which is an inverse of an exponential growth rate. It forces on everyone a very short-term point of view. This has been one of the main reasons why our technological advances have landed us so far in the soup; and it presents one of the major difficulties in seeing how we can plan more sensibly for a reasonably long-term future.

*Accelerated Exponential Growth*

This is simple exponential growth; but there can be, and often are, even more accelerated types of growth, which one might call second- or third-order types. One sort of second-order growth would be if the fraction of the existing system added on after each interval itself increased, as for instance in a human population in which health conditions were improving so that more of the babies born survived. In the example drawn in 5b.2, it has been assumed that the factor of increase after each interval increases by $\frac{1}{2}$ at each step, so that they go 2, $2\frac{1}{2}$, 3, $3\frac{1}{2}$ ... This results in the numbers in the system being 1, 2, 5, 15, $52\frac{1}{2}$ ... instead of 1, 2, 4, 8, 16 ... as they would be with simple exponential growth.

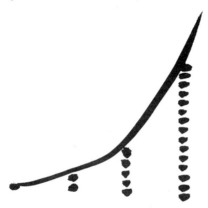

Fig. 5b.2

69

Another type of second-order acceleration is produced if each unit in the system is growing larger at the same time as the system is growing in numbers; for instance, each person in a population is demanding more and more of something, such as steel, as time passes. In 5b.3, the numbers in the population grow in a standard exponential way, 1, 2, 4, 8, 16 ... but each individual's size is enlarged by 50 per cent at each step, going 1, 1·5, 2·25, 3·375 ...

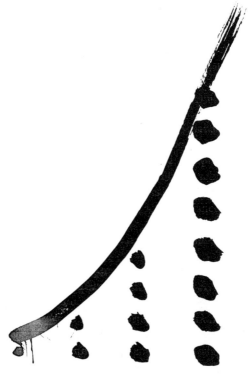

Fig. 5b.3

Of course, if one puts two second-order exponential growths together, to get a third-order system, it grows with enormous acceleration – this is what is happening, for instance, in demands on resources, in many parts of the world today.

*Limits to Growth*

Another very dramatic result of exponential growth occurs when it happens in some system which has natural limits that will eventually bring it to a stop. There is a well-known story of a farmer who noticed a water-lily on his pond, which doubled its size every day. To start with, of course, it covered only a very small area of the pond, and the farmer said to hell with it. Eventually it got quite big, and covered a fairly sizeable area, but the farmer said, 'Oh well, I won't do anything about it until it covers half the pond.' But when it did cover half the pond, how long had he got to cope with it? – exactly one day, of course. The crunch comes very fast under such circumstances. It comes even faster in the still more realistic situation in which the growing system removes something necessary for its growth from the environment, so that the environment is effectively getting smaller as the system is growing. Then the crunch between the rising size of the system and the decreasing size of its container comes even faster. This is the kind of situation which some people have supposed to apply to man's use of the limited raw materials of his Space-Ship Earth.

Drawing 5b.4 shows a situation in which a population is growing exponentially, and using up natural resources from a fixed stock at a constant rate per person. Obviously, eventually they will have used up all the resources there are; the only surprising point to note is how rapidly the situation deteriorates towards the end.

FIG. 5b.4

Clearly if resources are given once and for all, they must eventually be used up, however slowly they are consumed. It is only possible to achieve a stable system which can carry on indefinitely if new resources can be produced and added continuously to the initial stock. Then the system can become stable when resources are used at the same rate as they are produced. Drawing 5b.5 shows an example of what will happen if a population uses up its initial stock of resources much faster than they can be replaced. There will be an upsurge of numbers while the

Fig. 5b.5

initial stock is being used, followed by a rapid fall back to the numbers which the continuous production of resource can support.

As implied by the last two examples, exponential growth can go on indefinitely only when there are infinite space and raw materials available for it. This is never the case in the real world. Growth has been most fully studied in biological systems consisting of cells of animals or plants. The simple situation of exponential growth is an ideal which is really very difficult to achieve in practice. It is not only that growing systems soon begin to be limited by the size of the container – that is, the amount of space and raw materials available to it – but there are two other factors. The system is bound to produce a certain amount of waste products which it cannot itself utilize, and which in fact are likely to be harmful to it. Then again, the mechanisms of growth, by which the new materials are brought into being, tend to wear out and become less efficient as time goes on.

If we look at the actual growth that one is likely to find in a real biological system, what we see is a curve much more like 5b.6. There is often a short period at the beginning, known as the lag phase, in which

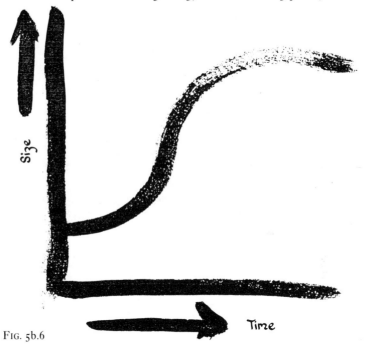

FIG. 5b.6

the system is adapting itself to its new surroundings. Then it may grow for a time exponentially. This period is commonly known as the log phase, because it is a mathematical consequence of the exponential formula, that the logarithm of the size appears as a straight line when it is plotted as a graph against the time. This has been done in 5b.7, and the log phase is quite recognizable as the straight line part, on the left. But eventually the rate of growth begins to slacken, the curve of size begins to rise less steeply, and then turns over and becomes flat. If it had gone on indefinitely in exponential growth the graph of the size would have been J-shaped. In practice it is nearly always S-shaped,

73

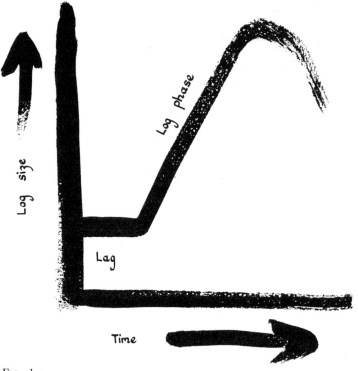

FIG. 5b.7

because if the system is in any finite container it is bound to generate forces which will slow up the growth and prevent it from going on to infinity.

These forces may under some circumstances act, as it were, gently, to produce a smooth transition from the exponential rate into a slower rate and an eventual stationary situation. Quite often, however, they will act in a way which one might consider less well balanced. A system may for a time grow bigger than the environment can continue to sustain, and will then undergo a period of rather vigorous de-growth (see 5b.8); there may in fact be several oscillations, of periods of growth followed by periods of de-growth, before it settles down to a stable size which the resources of the environment can maintain indefinitely. It is the possibility of such transient oscillations which has been one of the main subjects of study by Meadows, Meadows, Randers, and Behrew in their book *The Limits to Growth for the Club of Rome*.

There have been many attempts to find a suitable mathematical for-

74

FIG. 5b.8

mula to express the S-shaped curve; but although the turning over of
the curve at the top right is always produced by some sort of limitation
in the environment, or by a gradual wearing out of the growth machinery, in practice it takes so many different forms that no one formula is
appropriate in all cases. It is perhaps worth mentioning just one of the
best known of these formulae, which is derived from the idea that the
growing system depends on a store of some natural resource which it
uses up at a rate proportional to its own size. This is what is called the
'logistic' form of growth, which gives an S-shaped curve with the rather
complicated formula $\frac{1}{x}\frac{dx}{dt} = a - bx$. It often provides quite a good
description of many biological systems, but by no means all of them.

## Differential Growth

We have so far spoken as if the growing system were homogeneous, that is to say, all of one kind. But most growing systems have a number of different parts, and these parts may grow at different rates. For instance, different sections or groups in a human population may have different reproductive rates or death rates. The numbers of people in different types of employment may grow at different rates, depending on the development of industry and so on. There is no point in going into all the complexities that may arise; but there is one relatively simple system, which often happens in biological entities and may have some application in human affairs also. This is one in which the growth rate of one part is a more or less constant multiple of the growth rate of some other part, or of the whole. This produces what is known as 'hetero-gonic' growth. It occurs, for instance, in an animal which possesses particular organs which grow faster than the rest of the body (e.g. 5b.9).

FIG. 5b.9

The antlers of deer are often cited as examples; the bigger the body of the deer, the disproportionately bigger will be the antlers. A few mil-lennia ago there was a giant elk inhabiting Ireland. Its evolution seems to have been in the direction of becoming a larger and larger animal, possibly because the males fought with one another to capture females. By the time it became extinct and disappeared from the scene, the fully-grown animals had become very large; and this meant that their antlers, which grew in a heterogonic relation to the rest of the body, had become really gigantic. It is often suggested that it was the overdevelopment of these antlers, whose size rendered them a genuine handicap, that led to the extinction of this species. Perhaps we are seeing something rather similar in the development of motorways and parking places in the centre of cities; they are increasing in area so much faster than the rest of the city that they seem to be in danger of usurping the whole space, leaving nowhere for the houses and offices to go.

When different parts of a biological organism grow at different rates, the situation is often better described, not by dissecting the animal into separate organs and considering the growth rate of each one of these separately, but rather by saying that there are one or several *gradients* of growth. When a human baby is born its head is disproportionately large and its legs disproportionately small, compared to the relative sizes they will have when the child is an adult. During childhood, however, there is a general gradient of growth, so that the lower end (the legs) is growing fastest, and the upper end, the head, is growing slowest, and therefore the proportions of the body gradually change (5b.10).

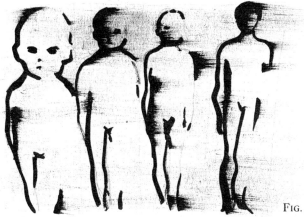

Fig. 5b.10

When one compares the adult forms of closely related species, one often finds that the shape of one could be changed into the shape of the other, if one were to suppose that different systems of growth gradients had been involved in the development of the animal. One way of exhibiting this is to draw the outline of one of the animals in a straightforward rectangular grid; then, if this grid is stretched or bent as though it had been drawn on a sheet of rubber, it can often be converted into another grid into which the shape of the other species would fit. This is sometimes a useful way of comparing complex shapes, as in 5b.11, to supplement the other methods discussed in Chapter 3.

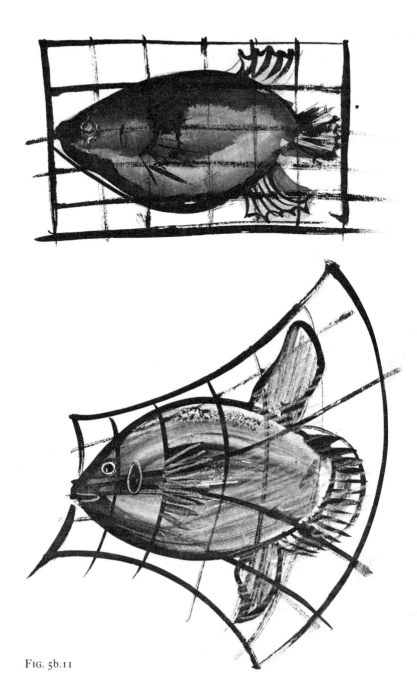

Fig. 5b.11

In the last few paragraphs we have considered growing things consisting of different parts, which may grow at different rates. When biologists have really tried to get down to considering the growth of an animal or plant in detail, they have had to realize that the growing system is always heterogeneous in a much finer-grained way than these considerations of overall shape and total weight imply. For instance the humans who are drawn in 5b.10 in outline really consist of bones, muscle, intestines and a whole lot of other parts; and each of these parts is made of innumerable cells of different kinds. Some cells may grow by actually increasing the amount of living substance; but others may increase in size by laying down deposits of mineral substances, such as the calcium carbonate of bones. Or again, they may swell merely by absorbing water.

Any discussion on overall growth simply obscures these actual details of what is happening. If one wants for some reason to talk of overall growth, then one must be content with some more or less arbitrarily chosen index, in which the various detailed components are compounded in a reasonably satisfying way. For instance, one may talk of the increase in dry weight; in this the complexities due to absorbed water are avoided, but the index will include deposited non-living mineral material like calcium carbonate in bones or shells.

A very similar problem arises when we talk of the growth of the economy. The best one can do, to give an overall index of it, is to adopt some arbitrary formula in which all the components are compounded in some way that seems sensible for the purposes in hand. The Gross National Product is the formula usually adopted, but, like the dry weight of an animal, it takes into account certain aspects of the situation but leaves out others; and the question must always be asked whether it reflects adequately the factors in which we are most interested in a particular context.

# 6   Feed-back in Systems

## A. Sequences

In most of the open systems in which one is likely to be interested, the entering materials (the inputs) are processed through a number of stages before they finally emerge again as production or waste (the outputs). The most important ideas we need for thinking about complex systems are notions concerned with such processes and their interactions.

To start with the simplest case: consider a system in which there is only one input, and this is operated on in a sequence of steps from, say, A to B, to C, to D, to E, until it finally comes out of the system again as a product F. Even such a simple sequence of processes has some quite interesting properties. One can perhaps most easily picture them by using the analogy of water flowing into the system through a pipe into a container A from which it can flow out again through another pipe into a container B, then on through a series of pipes into containers C, D and E, where there is the final pipe leading to F (6a.1).

The amount that flows per minute from container C into container D depends both on the diameter of the pipe connecting C with D, and also on the head of water in C. Suppose that we have a set-up with a series of containers connected by pipes of different diameters, and a certain inflow into A to start with. It is clear that, provided the containers are tall enough, they will each fill up to a given level which is just sufficient to push incoming water out again, through the outlet pipe; the smaller the outlet pipe, the higher the head of water will have to be. When a system has been running for some time (and, as said before, provided the containers are tall enough), the whole thing will have settled down at appropriate levels in each container which will not alter thereafter provided the input remains the same.

If the input into A is increased or decreased then, of course, levels in all the containers would have to alter in an appropriate way to maintain the steady flow. When the system has settled down to deal with any

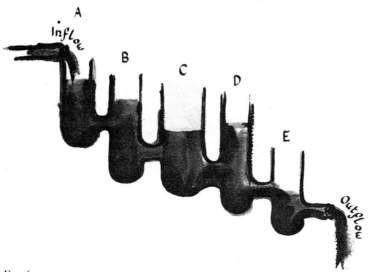

FIG. 6a.1

particular rate of input into A, it is said to have reached a stationary state. It is not, of course, stationary in the sense that nothing is happening – the water is flowing through it; but it is stationary in the sense that the level in each of the containers remains the same as long as the input is unchanged.

It is interesting to consider what would happen if we suddenly throttled down one of the pipes, say that between C and D (6a.2). What will eventually happen is clear enough: the water in C will rise until it is high enough to push the rate of flow through the narrower pipe into D so that it delivers the same amount per minute as it did before. Thus if the inflow remains constant, the outflow F will again be the same as it originally was, and all that will have changed will be the level of water in container C.

This situation is a simple example of a phenomenon often referred to as 'buffering' (a piece of technical jargon drawn from chemistry). In steady-state conditions the rate of outflow from F is buffered against changes in the diameters of the pipes connecting the various vessels – unless, of course, one pipe is so narrow that the head of water required to make the flow go fast enough through it is higher than the container it leads out of, in which case the system will eventually break down and this container will overflow unless the initial input at A is reduced. This character of 'being buffered against certain types of change' is one of the

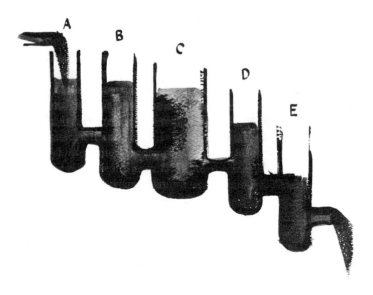

most interesting properties of systems and processes. From the practical point of view, some of the most important properties of systems, as we deal with them in real life, are the kinds and limitations of stability in their behaviour.

Note that the buffering we have considered so far concerns the condition reached when the system comes back again into a stationary state after a disturbance such as a narrowing of one of the connecting pipes. A number of changes may go on, some of them rather unexpected, before the new stationary state is reached. These changes are known as 'transients'. In practical affairs they also may be very important, particularly when one is dealing with long-life systems, such as human populations.

*Positive Feed-back*

The analogy, or model, of water flowing through a system which consists of fixed tanks and pipes is, of course, much too simple to represent most real living systems, in the biological or human or social worlds. In living things what we have compared to tanks and pipes are themselves manufactured within the system. Some of the initial input is used to make the tanks, and the controlling pipes connecting them, which other portions of the input flow through. In a living cell, for instance, part of the nutrients, oxygen and so on, taken in from its surroundings,

FIG. 6a.3

is converted into enzymes which control the rates at which another part of the input is converted into substance A, then B, C, D and so on. These enzymes therefore correspond to the pipes in our previous analogy (6a.3).

Since these 'pipes' are made within the system, the cell is perfectly able to bring about for itself a change in a particular rate of flow, so that an alteration corresponding to what we spoke of as 'throttling down a particular pipe' can be produced internally, and does not have to be imposed from outside. It is a very general observation, in all systems from cells through individuals to societies, that such internally produced changes often occur.

They do so in two different ways which have opposite effects. In one way, the more there is of a particular component, say D, the faster D is produced; D affects the earlier stages in the sequence to increase the rate of flow through them. This is known as *positive feed-back* (6a.4), and is a reinforcing type of action. It is clearly closely related to the self-stimulating type of process which results in exponential, or accelerated exponential, growth (p. 66), such as the situation in which the more young adults there are in a population, the more babies get added to it. But here we are considering the rather different case, in which the amount of some constituent in a sequence affects some earlier step in the

FIG. 6a.4

sequence, which may involve things of quite a different kind. For instance, after the number of people in a region of the earth's surface grows beyond a certain point, there can be some who are surplus to the requirement for agricultural work to produce food; and they can start building cities, and digging irrigation systems, and setting up windmills, and a whole lot of things which will eventually, through a number of steps, lead to an increase in the rate of growth of the human population. Where positive feed-back differs from exponential growth is that in the former we are dealing with sequences of different steps, and in the latter with only a single step.

*Chain Reactions*

Another related concept is the 'chain reaction'. The idea is a very simple one; so simple that it would have tempted Sherlock Holmes to say 'Elementary, my dear Watson.' So you might ask, why give it special discussion? The answer is that I think most people, much too often, just tend to forget it or leave it out of account. It is actually one of the most dangerous, or, if you play it right, one of the most rewarding, of the processes, dealing with which you have to spend your life.

A chain reaction is one which can occur when there is a sequence of steps; *a* goes to *b*, and *b* goes to *c*, and *c* to *d*, and *d* to *e* and so on and on. The phrase 'chain reaction' is used when there is a sort of multiplication at each step; a slight increase in *a* produces a bigger increase in *b*, and that a still bigger one in *c*, and that a really hefty jump in *d*. Each step in the series can (perhaps only after it gets above some threshold value) open a gate, or turn on a valve, which really lets the next step get going in a big way.

84

It's not a new idea. The classical statement of it, as far as my reading goes, was by Benjamin Franklin (in the pre-automobile era):

> For want of a nail the shoe was lost,
> For want of a shoe, the horse was lost,
> For want of a horse, the battle was lost,
> For loss of a battle, the kingdom was lost.

But, though it is both simple and old, the idea is of key importance. And, remember, it works in both directions. Never neglect to consider that what you are going to do now may spark off a chain reaction towards Utopia (I wouldn't bet too heavily on actually finding you get there), or trigger the first fuse for a succession of ever more devastating disasters (but a little bit of sense along the way can protect you better against finishing up in absolute hell than it can guarantee you a smooth progress to absolute heaven).

## Negative Feed-back

But very often restraining influences also arise within the system. It is by no means always the case that the presence of a lot of D encourages the formation of more D. Perhaps more often living things behave in a way which may be called 'satiation' or 'enough's as good as a feast'. That is to say, after some point is reached, the more D there is, the slower new D is formed. This is a *negative feed-back* (6a.5). It is a

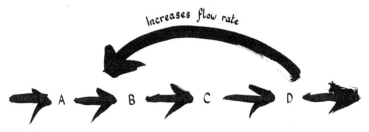

FIG. 6a.5

restraining type of action, and is the basic process that living things rely on to see that no one of their internal processes runs away and gets out of hand. It is also the kind of process incorporated into many man-made controlling devices. If the central heating pushes up the temperature of a room too far, the thermostat comes into play and shuts down the central heating, and reduces the input of heat into a room until the temperature gets back to the appropriate level.

Biologists make a distinction between two types of negative feed-back; and in social affairs there are analogies to these two kinds of process which originally described the level of cells and enzymes (6a.6).

Fig. 6a.6

The first, and in some ways the milder, form of feed-back is one in which the presence of one component in a chain, such as D, acts in some way to slow up the flow through an earlier step in the chain, say from B to C, by as it were throttling down that pipe to some extent. This is known as 'inhibition' – and since we can consider D the end product in the sequence we are talking about, it is often called 'end-product inhibition'.

The second and more drastic form of negative feed-back occurs in living systems in which the link between B and C (the 'pipe', or, in more real terms, the enzyme which brings about this chemical change) is actually manufactured within the system out of some of the incoming materials. The second type of feed-back does not merely reduce the efficiency of the enzyme between B and C, but actually abolishes its production, at least until the level of D drops low enough again. This is 'end-product repression'.

If a factory works very efficiently and produces a large output (of automobiles, say), and the workers conclude that the firm is making too large a profit, so they go on strike for more pay or shorter working hours, that would be end-product inhibition. But if, instead, they staged a revolution, sacked the management or destroyed the machine-tools, that would be end-product repression because they would be not merely slowing the production process but repressing the machinery of production. Similarly, if pupils in a school thought they were asked to learn too much and decided to work slowly, that would be inhibition; if they attacked the teachers, or burnt their books, that would be repression.

Inhibition usually produces its effects much faster than repression does. For instance, if there is a very high concentration of traffic using a certain road, the traffic flow will be slowed down by an inhibition which operates almost immediately. Repression would correspond to a situation in which, by some system of signalling, the traffic density controlled the flow into that road, for instance by diverting some along alternative routes. This might be more efficient in the long run, but obviously would take longer to produce its effect.

## B. Networks

One way in which the model we have been using so far is overly simplified, to represent the systems we meet in the real world, is that we have been talking about a single input which is processed through a series of changes into a single output. Of course, in most systems, such as our own bodies, input is of several different kinds – food consists of proteins, fats, carbohydrates, minerals and what have you, and the output is also of many kinds – more muscle, more kidney, more liver, more nerve, more excreta. The next step in making a more realistic picture is to think in terms of something like a tree diagram or dendrogram, such as we considered on p. 54. That is to say, the input gets parcelled out into a number of different branches which go off, dividing and dividing again, into a large number of different end results (6b.1).

But in most actual systems the input does not simply get split up along a whole set of divergent pathways, like the branches and twigs of a tree. These branches and twigs are in general not wholly independent even after they have split apart from each other. Pathways along which things are processed may have as their major characteristic a tree-like character, branching down from a main trunk to main limbs, to main branches, to twigs and so on; but along with this, and sometimes more

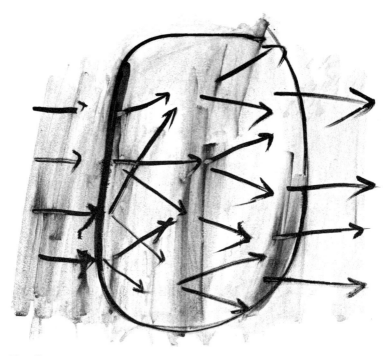

FIG. 6b.1

important, are interconnections between the branches and twigs. The pathways form a network, rather than a simple tree-like pattern (6b.2).

Within such networks there will be the same type of tendencies to de-stabilize the behaviour (by positive feed-back) or to stabilize it (by negative feed-back), as we saw in the simple unbranched sequences. If in such a network one of the channels of communications becomes constricted, the flow will just go round it, along one or more of the alternative pathways the network provides. In a single-channel sequence there is a certain buffering of the final throughput (p. 54); in a network this may work even more efficiently, and without requiring any very large changes in the level of storage in the early storage tanks along the way. Again, the level of some final output may act as a negative feed-back, repressing or even inhibiting some other link in the network, which need not be directly on the sequence leading to it.

For instance, in a city the presence of too many cars on the road does not operate directly to inhibit the production of new cars, or even to repress automobile manufacture in general, but rather to inhibit some

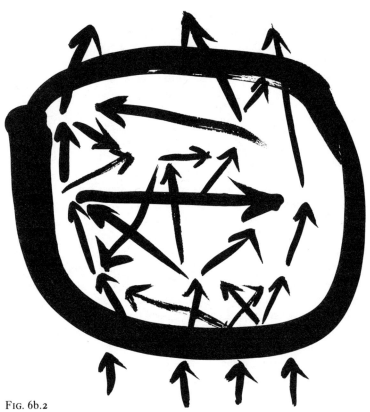

FIG. 6b.2

other part of the network, such as the tendency of people to move their houses out of the central cities into the suburbs. To give another example; in an ecosystem the existence of too many rabbits – above a certain limit – tends to reduce their rate of reproduction, because they get in each other's way and the females ready to bear young are always getting disturbed by aggressive males, and tend to abort or not look after their young adequately. But in a real ecosystem, long before these direct effects begin to be important, it is much more likely that the presence of such a large number of rabbits gives a field day to the foxes and other animals that live on the rabbits, so that they increase enough in number to keep the rabbit population down to a reasonable size. The indirect negative feed-back loop, number of rabbits through number of foxes to reduction of rabbit population, is likely to be more effective than the direct loop, too many rabbits interfering with each other's reproduction.

There is in fact what might be called a sort of 'inherent network-buffering'. The more complex a network is and the more it is interconnected, the more indifferent it is to the severing of any particular link. This is, however, only a very rough rule. The general theory of stability of networks is actually very little understood.

*Modelling Networks*

Ideally, one would aim at specifying all the reactions going on in a network, measuring their rate and the strengths of the interactions between them, and then putting these data together into a system of equations from which one could calculate the response of the system to any given disturbance. Usually, in practice, it is impossible to make such a complete analysis. The difficulties are likely to be partly in measuring the rates of reactions and interactions, and partly that the sheer complexity of the system may make the equations impossible to handle by normal mathematical methods. The advent of computers has largely overcome the latter difficulty, since with their great speed at doing simple arithmetic, they can be programmed to solve even the most formidable set of equations in a reasonably short time.

But the difficulty of estimating the parameters (rates of reactions and interactions) can usually only be circumvented in rather unsatisfactory ways. One can start by using the best estimates and informed guesses that are available, both about these values and about the structure of linkages within the network. Then one can try out the response of the system, as calculated by the computer, against any data about the actual response which can be collected. In the situations most favourable for analysis, it may be possible to apply known disturbances to the system, and to observe and measure its responses; if they are not quite what the computer predicts, one would have to change either the structure of the model, or some of the values fed into it, or both, till there was a better agreement between the computed and actual behaviour.

Another, usually less informative, way of testing a model, is to compare its results with the past history of the system, if one has good data about this. For instance, in a model of an economic system, whose history has been recorded in good statistics, one might use the past twenty years of history to work out, by gradual approximations, a model and set of values which predict the actual behaviour over that period; and one would have some degree of confidence that the same model might foretell how the system would behave in the next few years.

However, even in a field like economics, in which there are very good statistics covering quite long periods, it has proved very difficult to make models which predict accurately for more than a very short time ahead.

One of the main results of such studies so far has in fact been to show that complex network systems behave in very unexpected ways. Their behaviour has been described as 'counter-intuitive', in the sense that if one makes some changes to the system with the intention of producing a certain effect, the actual response often turns out to be something quite unanticipated. Sometimes these counter-intuitive results occur only in the short run; they may be caused by some parts of the system approaching a new equilibrium by an oscillatory path instead of a smooth path (see Fig. 6b.2), or by some other transient phenomenon of that kind. But sometimes they are due to a breakdown in some apparently unrelated but fragile part of the system. To give an excessively simple example, a throttling down of one of the taps in Fig. 6a.2 might raise the water level in one of the tanks earlier in the system to the level at which it overflowed.

It is, perhaps, in the revealing of these unexpected and still little-understood types of behaviour of systems that the computer models have been most useful so far; but one may hope that they will gradually be improved until they are more reliable in predicting actual details of behaviour rather than merely indicating types of response which one must be on the look-out for. Chapter 12 is concerned with attempts to build up this kind of model of the whole world system.

Meanwhile, one usually has to be content, in handling many systems, with much cruder methods and ideas.

*Soft Spots*

In most networks, alterations at some places are likely to have more profound effects on the system than alterations at others; moving one particular item from a house of cards may bring the whole thing tumbling down, whereas removing many other items may have much less effect. If one is trying to alter a system which has some inbuilt buffering, one of the important first steps is to try to locate these 'soft spots'. There has been a good deal of theoretical discussion about how to locate them, or preferably how to measure the sensitivity of each particular link in the network. The most important result to emerge is that the sensitivity of a particular link is not a fixed characteristic of it, but depends on the state of the rest of the network. In some states of the system, the soft spot will be in one place; and in a different state it may be somewhere else. For instance, in providing housing in a city one is dealing with a system which involves many components. In some circumstances it may be that the practical issue is to provide new sites for housing in desired locations; in others it may be the provision of capital, or suitable labour and so on. The contribution of each particular item to the stability or changeableness of the system changes as the system itself changes.

## C. Lock-in, Schismogenesis and Double-bind

One may find oneself confronted with systems which have no obvious soft spots. They seem like an iron ring, or a vicious circle, from which it is impossible to escape. There are some recently introduced ideas and phrases which are often useful in this connection.

The first is 'lock-in'. A lock-in is a situation in which in the beginning component a interacts with a number of other components, b, c, d, etc., but the interaction with one of these, say c, sets off a reaction which in some way tends to confine a's attention to c; so that as the situation develops, a comes to be reacting only with c, all his other reactions having petered out, a is 'locked in'. (The lock-in loop need not have only

Time 1
Lock - in

Time 2
Lock - in

Fig. 6c.1

two members, a and c; it may be a lock-in to the group a, c, e (6c.1); the point is that the interactions become limited to a small number of all those possible.) One often meets such a situation in discussions; a general political discussion may get locked in to a dispute about the merits of the doctrines of Lenin, Trotsky and Stalin. As this example suggests, lock-ins usually get nowhere; they may engender a lot of heat but little light, or they may fade out in a paralysis of boredom.

The next notion, which was introduced by the anthropologist-psychologist Gregory Bateson, has the rather daunting name 'schismogenesis', a word which means the development of a chasm or cleft. Basically it involves two parties, a and b, and it is a situation in which what one party does provokes the other to go further in the behaviour to which the first party is reacting. There are two varieties of it. In one, the two parties are behaving to each other in essentially the same way. Competing for keeping up with the Joneses, purchasing ever better, more splendid automobiles or other articles of competitive display, would be a good example. An arms race between two opposing nations is another instance. This is *symmetrical schismogenesis*; a takes a step in a certain direction and this provokes b to take a longer step in the same direction, which provokes a to go still further, and so on and on (6c.2).

FIG. 6c.2

In the other kind, the two components act in opposite ways. A relation of authority and subservience is an example. The dominant partner assumes a somewhat bullying attitude, and the other person accepts it so humbly that this provokes the dominant one to become even more masterful, which again increases the subservience of the other and so on. This is *complementary* schismogenesis (6c.3).

FIG. 6c.3

A third notion, also largely due to Bateson, is the 'double-bind'. Here three components are involved in such a manner that the way in which a reacts with b inevitably has the result of making it more difficult for him to react properly with c. It is common in psycho-social situations. If a child loves his mother enough, this is taken by his father as disloyalty to him; so he increases his efforts to attract the child's affection; and then the mother redoubles hers. Or a child may be told he has to meet two incompatible goals – being always polite and always saying exactly what he thinks; and as soon as he does one, he is reminded that he should be doing the other. Or a townsman wants to get back to nature, but the more he lives in a countrified suburb, the more he has to commute by car and the less he can walk (6c.4).

FIG. 6c.4

The lock-in and schismogenesis situations are closely connected, in logical structure, with some of the non-zero-sum games we discuss later, such as 'Prisoner's Dilemma' (p. 167) and the 'Tragedy of the Commons'. An amusing example of a locked-in symmetrical schismogenesis in the form of a game is 'Auction-A-Dollar', invented by Martin Shubik (see John Platt, *Social Traps*). The auctioneer draws up the rules, which are that bidding is to start at five cents; the bids must increase by at least five cents at a time; and, since it seems at first sight that someone might get the dollar really cheap, he lays it down that he is to be given the two highest bids, although only the one highest bidder will receive the dollar. What will happen? It is all plain sailing until the bidding gets to forty-five cents, and then to fifty cents. From this point if it goes any higher, to fifty-five cents, the auctioneer is going to get more than his dollar back. But if it does not go higher, then the man who bid forty-five cents is going to give it over and get nothing back; so he raises his bid. By the time the bidding gets to a dollar, the man who bid ninety-five cents is in an even nastier situation; if he raises to $1.05 he will lose money even if he gets the dollar at that price; but he will lose a lot more if he lets the bidding stop; so up he goes. John Platt warns that it is a dangerous game to play; the lock-in escalation is so tight that it may wreck friendships, perhaps permanently. The way to escape, of course, would be for the players to make some side-arrangement, outside the rules of the game, such that they would stop bidding at some early stage, below fifty cents, and would agree to split the dollar between the two highest bidders; then both would have made a profit. We shall see later, in discussing Prisoner's Dilemma, that communication and agreement between players is one of the most effective ways of escape from many such situations.

There seem to be only two ways, apart from collaboration between some of the participants, of dealing with these vicious-circle-type systems, which have no obvious soft spots. One way is to try to alter all the links in the network of cause and effect simultaneously. The other is to look at the wider context in which the vicious-circle system is embedded, and try within that to discover some other system which can be brought into such powerful operation, that the contribution of the vicious circle to the whole set-up becomes of reduced importance, so that it can be forgotten and left to wither away with lapse of time. Perhaps the only possible solution to the schismogenic arms race between the US and the USSR will emerge by the transference, by both of them, of their main interests to a quite different topic – the issues of environment, pollution, natural resources and the whole World Problematique.

This chapter has described the important types of interaction between different components in complex systems. Some of these interactions, like positive feed-back, or schismogenesis, tend to reinforce or speed up processes of change, and they therefore are liable to 'run away' and get out of control. Other interactions, like the different kinds of negative feed-back, or network buffering, or lock-ins, tend to slow things up and thus to control them. If we regard complex systems as things we would like to manage, these controlling activities are particularly important, especially those which do not necessarily involve a narrowing of the field of interaction, as lock-ins do. The next chapter will be devoted to the various forms the control of complex systems may take.

# 7 Stabilization in Complex Systems

The last but one chapter, about the processes in complex systems, may have left some of the more faint-hearted readers with the feeling that all such systems are bound just to get into a mess, and stay that way. But actually one has only to look at, say, the movements of a ballet dancer, or even a reasonably healthy person walking about, to realize that systems which would appear enormously complicated if examined in detail, can behave with considerable overall simplicity. Messages are going along many different nerves, from the brain to the muscles, and from the limbs back to the brain; subtle acts of balance are being carried out continuously; dozens of muscles in the legs and arms are contracting, and other dozens relaxing, at every step. But all these actions are balanced out against each other, so that the system as a whole behaves in a 'sensible', unitary way, which we can call 'walking', or even a beautifully coordinated way we call 'dancing'. This chapter will try to describe some of the general principles by which complex systems become organized so that the complexity does not obtrude and there is an overall unity of action. The ideas involved are, of course, rather general ones. It is much easier to grasp particular details than to comprehend the way those details merge together to give rise to the organization of the system. I warned that this book would provide some challenges to the imagination of its readers; this chapter has its full share of them.

The study of the processes discussed here is often referred to by the name cybernetics, and the adjective 'cybernetic' describes the character of the processes. This is a very general term, and to get much understanding of the situation one has to go into it in a bit more detail.

We need to distinguish first between systems which come to some sort of end-state in which they remain constant or go on repeating themselves indefinitely, and on the other hand systems which go on changing as long as one cares to observe them. The former can be called terminating systems, and the latter progressive systems.

# A. Terminating Systems and Stable States

We have already mentioned the possibility that a situation finally gets into a steady state, and pointed out that this does not mean that nothing is happening, but merely that some sort of flow is going steadily through the system. What remains stationary is the pattern of this flow. Any end-state which a system attains, or moves towards, is sometimes referred to as a 'goal'; but that is a rather anthropomorphic usage.

There are, however, several other types of terminal states. In the first place, the system may be one which really holds constant some particular component, as a thermostat holds constant the temperature of a room. There are many components in an animal's body which are held constant in a similar way. An example is the carbon dioxide content of one's blood. When you take a lot of exercise, the fuel used up to power the muscles releases carbon dioxide in solution into the blood. Various parts of the body mechanism then change in rate (heartbeat, breathing, etc.) in such a way as to clear the excess carbon dioxide out of the blood and bring its concentration back to the normal level. The constancy of the $CO_2$ level in the blood, or the temperature in a room controlled by a thermostat, are examples of steady states. The technical word for the process of returning to a steady-state system after it has been disturbed is 'homeostasis' (from two Greek words, meaning 'the same' and 'state').

In well-organized systems such as the human body there are homeostatic mechanisms which can control several variables at once. In the blood, it is not only the concentration of $CO_2$ which is kept constant, but also the acidity, the level of oxygen, the level of several salts and so on. Thinking about, or visualizing, things which involve many components simultaneously is, of course, not easy to do, but this is one of the main tasks which one has to attempt when trying to comprehend complex systems. It can be done accurately in terms of fairly elaborate mathematics; but one can get some sort of a general imaginative picture of the situation, if one is willing to use a little imagination, and does not demand too much logical precision.

Everyone knows that one of the standard mathematical ways to express a relation between two things, x and y, is to make a graph of them. A graph of x against y can be drawn on a flat sheet of paper, with the value of x measured off from the point of origin from left to right, and the value of y measured vertically upwards. If you were to take account of another variable, z, you have to add a third axis at right-angles to the other two, and the point representing the simultaneous values of all three components is located somewhere inside a three-dimensional space (7a.1).

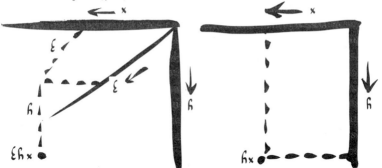

FIG. 7a.1

Now if you were to try to picture a homeostatic mechanism, which restores the concentrations of x and y and z to some particular values after the system has been disturbed, how could you do it? One could say that the homeostatic mechanism produces some sort of controlling activities which have the result that if the x, y, z is displaced from its normal position the activities push it back there again. One can visualize these controlling activities in the form of an imaginary 'attractor surface' in the shape of a cone, its point downwards and located at the normal position of x, y and z. If the x, y and z point is pushed upwards into some other position, it is first attracted back on to this surface (as though the surface was a magnet which pulled in a little iron ball corresponding to the displaced point); and once it has got on to the cone it runs down it to the bottom and finds itself back at its normal position (7a.2).

The language of mathematics is such that it is quite easy to deal not only with a point representing three variables, which can be in real three-dimensional space, but also with a point representing very many variables, which would have to be located in a multi-dimensional space that is impossible for the human mind to visualize. However, even without mathematics, by thinking in terms of attractor surfaces in three dimensions, we can get some notions about the types of stability which may be exhibited by systems in which there are many more than three variables being controlled simultaneously. We shall use this type of imagery when we go on to discuss more complex systems. Before doing that, it is necessary to mention some other types of end-states which terminating systems may eventually reach.

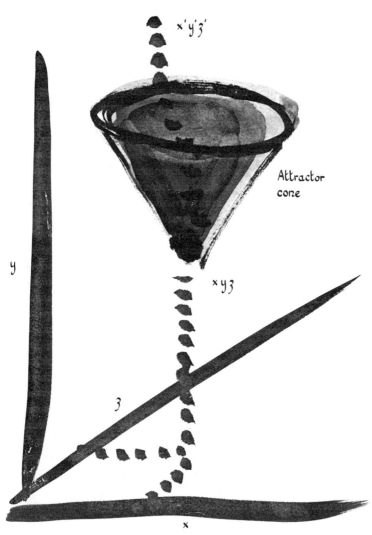

x'y'3'

Attractor
cone

xy3

y

3

x

FIG. 7a.2

Perhaps the most striking other type of end-state is one in which the system continues to oscillate regularly between two extremes. The pattern of the system never settles down and stays put, but in its end-state it is still subject to a 'swing of the pendulum' phenomenon. We can draw this either as an unending wavy line which goes on and on as time passes (7a.3), or one can draw a circular loop connecting the two extremes, and say that the system goes round and round this loop, which is referred to as a 'limit cycle' (7a.4).

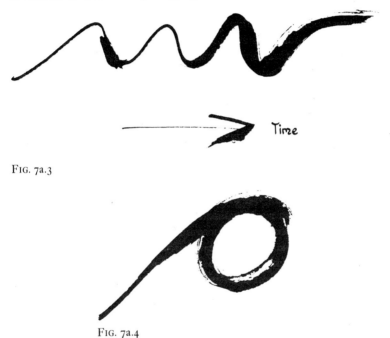

Time

FIG. 7a.3

FIG. 7a.4

Another variety of end-state, which could perhaps be thought of as a progressive rather than a terminating system, is one in which the system tends towards a stationary state but never quite gets there. If, for instance, some measure of a variable in a system, say the numbers in a population, grows along an S-shaped curve, it will, during the second part, be increasing more and more slowly; the rate of increase may finally become almost imperceptible, but if examined sufficiently closely the population would still be growing. If one has good enough measurements, one can calculate the limit it would get to if it was left to grow for an infinite time; this is known as the asymptote (7a.5).

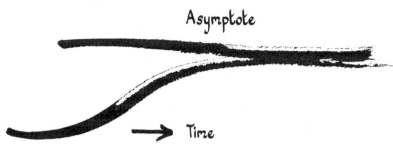

Asymptote

Time

FIG. 7a.5

Other systems may approach the asymptote not steadily, or more and more slowly, but by swinging above and below it at continually decreasing intervals. This is an oscillatory approach to the final value. Another way to picture it is to let the system get almost into a limit cycle, but one in which the radius of the circle gradually gets smaller, so that the system is in effect spiralling gradually inwards (7a.6).

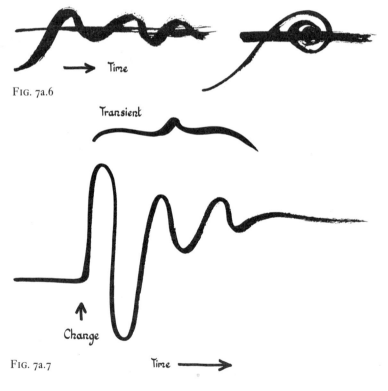

Time

FIG. 7a.6

Transient

Change

FIG. 7a.7            Time ⟶

# B. Progressive Systems and Stable Flows

Consideration of the way terminating systems approach their end-state leads on to a discussion of progressive systems, which either do not have an end-state, or at least are so far away from it that it can be neglected. Probably most systems that we have to deal with in the human and social world are of this kind, either because they involve time-intervals which are very long in human terms (such as the growth of human populations), or because they are small parts of ecosystems which are also changing, so that the inputs into the smaller system will have altered before it has been able to reach its end-state.

Any initial set of inputs into a progressive system will produce a sequence of changes; but these are very difficult to decide precisely. This is one of the fields in which modern mathematics, powerful though it is, remains rather helpless. It is often possible, if one knows sufficient about a system, to calculate what its end-state will be, but it is very much more difficult to get any precise picture of the changes that will go on as it gets there.

Though precise mathematics may not be able to solve the equations which show the paths along which the systems will change, we can sometimes get an indication of them by exploiting the fantastic rapidity with which the computer can carry out arithmetical calculations. If, for instance, we have a system with five components, a, b, c, d and e, and if we know the values of the measurements of these components, and also the strength of the interaction between each component and all the others, and how those interactions will change as the whole state of the system changes (as the soft spots changed, as we discuss on p. 105), we could write down systems of equations which would describe the way the system would alter. And even if we could not solve these equations by algebra (as we usually can't), a computer could hammer out a solution step by step, using the first set of values to calculate the values a small time later, then those again to calculate the next step, and so on. This is the procedure which has been used by the Club of Rome team, at MIT, to investigate the 'World System' (see Chapter 12).

The cautions which we shall have to express when we discuss this work bring out the dangers in the application of methods of this kind. The main snags are these. Even if we have got reliable figures for the present measurements of the components into which the system is analysed, we usually have only quite unreliable estimates of the strengths of their interactions. And we usually have almost no notion of how these strengths of interactions are going to change as the system itself changes. In such circumstances it is quite unsafe to accept the results of the computer calculations as anything like reliable predictions of what the system will in fact do. The best we can really hope for is that the computer will illustrate *types* of behaviour which we had not intuitively thought of as being likely.

This in fact is what it often does. It shows that if we change some aspect of a system of this kind, the first result will often be a lot of other changes where we didn't expect them, although if the system is left alone long enough, it might settle down to a terminal, or more or less terminal, stage, which had something like the character we were aiming at when we made the alteration in the first place. It is rather as though, in the model of water flowing through a system of containers, which we discussed on p. 80, you found that if you suddenly threw an extra bucket of water into one of the containers all the others went through a series of unexpected risings and fallings, before they settled down to their new values.

These immediate responses to changes in the system variables may be considered as 'transients'. Given a long enough time after the change in the system, transient changes will be smoothed out into some new, perhaps only slightly altered, pattern of relationships between the values of the components. However, when we are dealing with systems whose responses take a long time in terms of human lifetime, such as the world system of human populations, food production and so on, transients might last for periods of many decades, and might involve changes in variables as important as the total numbers of the population.

Computer results have in fact made the important point that the first transient responses of a system to a change in the measure of one of its components, or a change of the coefficient of interaction between components, will often be of a kind that one was not expecting at all: it may be 'counter-intuitive'. So far there has been very little study of these counter-intuitive transients, and a great deal more work is needed before we can feel we have a grasp of how the system is likely to respond to any given change.

In many systems we come across, some type of stability has been an important property. A natural living system has usually acquired some degree of stability by natural selection (it would have fallen apart and died out if it wasn't stable enough); in artificial systems man commonly designs a series of checks and counter-checks to ensure stability. An important point to note, however, is that the stability may not be concerned to preserve the measure of some component of the system at a constant value, as in the homeostatic systems mentioned earlier. The stabilization of a progressive system acts to ensure that the system goes on altering in the same sort of way that it has been altering in the past. Whereas the process of keeping something at a stable, or stationary, value is called homeo*stasis*, ensuring the continuation of a given type of change called homeo*rhesis*, a word which means preserving a flow.

One can picture a homeorhetic system in terms of an attractor surface (which again is located in a multidimensional space, so that one again has to form rather an intuitive picture of it, rather than a precise delineation). In this case the surface cannot be a cone leading to a point. What the control mechanisms are bringing about is a continual change along a certain pathway. The surface has, therefore, to be more or less the shape of a valley; the stabilized pathway of change is like a stream bed running along the bottom of the valley. The point which represents the measurements of the components at any given time will be, as it were, a little ball rolling down the valley bottom, which has reached a certain place (A) at the time in question. If then something is done which displaces this ball to A′, it will in the first place be attracted back to the attractor surface, and hit the hillside somewhere up the side of the valley (B). Since it will have been rolling down the valley bottom, it will have some momentum to carry on travelling in that direction. It will, therefore, not run straight down the hillside to the nearest place on the valley bottom, but will run down at a slant, reaching the bottom (C) somewhere ahead of where it started (7b.1).

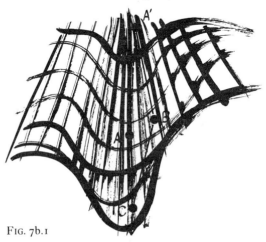

FIG. 7b.1

This is the sort of behaviour one very often sees in developing systems. If, for instance, injury is made to an embryo at an early stage in its development, it is often found that eventually a normal later embryo develops; the system can 'regulate' and restore itself to normality, and carry on to the normal end result. However, after injury, it does not just go back to where it was at the time of damage, and carry on from there; it gets itself gradually back on course, so that the damage is not restored until the embryo has developed to a later stage than that at which the damage was first done.

## Chreods and Epigenetic Landscapes

Another phrase used to describe such systems, is to say that the pathway of change is canalized. For the pathway itself one can use the name *chreod*, a word derived from Greek, which means 'necessary path'. Many types of change going on in society have a more or less well-developed chreodic character; once they have got well started in a certain direction, it is very difficult to divert them.

Different canalized pathways or chreods may have rather different types of stability built into them. These can be pictured in terms of the cross-section of the valley. You may, for instance, have a valley with a very narrow chasm running along the bottom, while the farther up the hillside you go, the less steep the slope; with such a configuration of the attractor surface, it needs a very strong push of some kind to divert a stream away from the bottom of the chasm (7b.2). If the system is acted

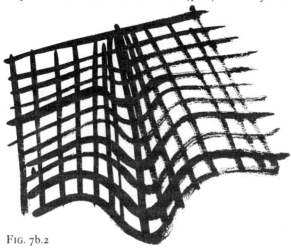

FIG. 7b.2

106

on by only rather minor disturbances, it is likely always to stay very close to the bottom of the valley. If one can compare several examples of such a system, there will be very little difference between them, and they will look very invariable. In contrast, we have a valley which has a very flat bottom, and the hillside gets steeper and steeper as you go away from the central stream (7b.3). Then, minor disturbances can easily shunt the stream from one side of the flat valley bottom to the other; it would be rather a matter of chance where in the water-meadows in the valley bottom it flows. If one looks at a number of examples of a system with this type of stability, there will be a lot of small-scale variation between them.

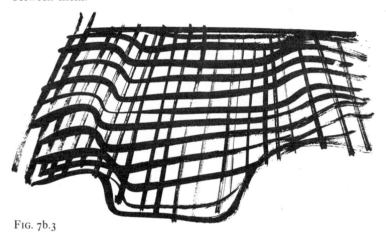

FIG. 7b.3

As an example of what the idea of chreods, or canalization, means in an everyday context, consider the accumulation of wealth in a community. Any individual receives some income and has some outgoings; his wealth grows or diminishes according to the difference between these. In the well-known words of Dickens' (pre-decimalization) character Mr Micawber: 'Annual income £20, annual expenditure £19. 19. 6., result happiness. Annual income £20, annual expenditure £20. 0. 6., result misery.'

Translating into a visual representation, and adding a bit of mathematical jargon, we can draw a diagram with wealth measured upwards from the base-line, and time flowing from left to right. An individual at any given time has a certain wealth, and this is represented by a corresponding point; but his current bank balance is affected by his income and his outgoings, and as time passes it will move along a line, horizontally if he keeps them exactly in balance, upwards if he is getting richer, downwards if he is getting poorer. Such lines are known as *vectors*, and the whole area of the diagram is a *vector-field* (7b.4).

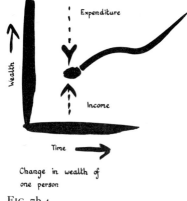

Change in wealth of one person

Fig. 7b.4

It is unfortunately common experience that in our society, and in many like it, the rich tend to get richer, and the poor poorer. So if we start with a population of people with varied incomes, the vector-field tends to look like this (7b.5):

Fig. 7b.5 Vector field for many persons

A tendency towards canalization, or the formation of chreods in such a system, would occur if there were forces at work tending to limit the steepest increases, or the most drastic reductions, in the wealth of individuals. In practice we do have such forces in Britain, e.g. steeply rising surtax of large incomes and welfare benefits added to low ones. In their simplest form, such forces might act to produce a 'rich, but not too rich, chreod', and a 'poor, but not too poor' one (7b.6(A)). Actually, the controlling forces are more complex, and tend to result in several rather

108

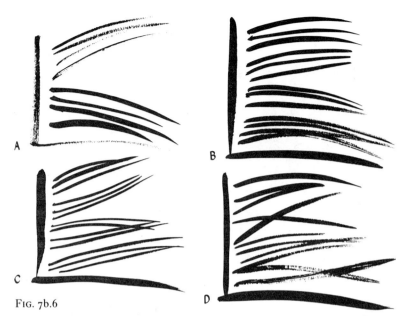

FIG. 7b.6

than only two wealth classes (B). We would like, of course, to put into operation forces acting within the vector-field in such a way that no one actually ever gets any poorer (C). And then, a further step, provisions that make it reasonably easy for individuals to move over from one chreod to another, preferably stepping up rather than down (D). Or, of course, we might try to set up a non-chreodic system, which did not tend to produce distinct classes at all, but at the same time prevented gross differences in wealth, and an overall upward trend.

In progressive biological systems, such as developing embryos or plants, one is usually confronted with a system which cannot be fully described in terms of a single chreod, or even collections of roughly parallel chreods, as is seen in the wealth diagrams. When an egg is developing, different parts of it will follow different courses of development, and eventually finish up forming different parts of the final animal: some parts becoming muscle, some becoming nerve and so on. This can be pictured in terms of an 'epigenetic landscape', in which when the process starts there is a single valley, but this later branches into two or more, and these branches split up again and again, until they have formed a number of separate valleys corresponding to the separate parts of the adult animal (7b.7).

Many progressive systems in fields other than biology behave in a similar way. For instance, when a town is beginning to grow into a city,

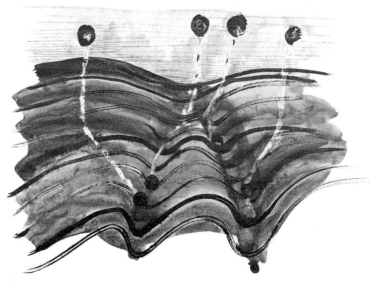

at first it is likely that it will all be following one and the same path of change, related to a single city centre. Later on some sub-centres will develop, or suburbs will be founded, and the single pathway of change will have become diversified into a number of subsidiary paths.

Again, consider the historical development of some type of thinking, such as Christianity or Marxism. It starts with a single line of development, and later splits up into a number of more or less divergent paths of change, such as the Orthodox and Catholic churches, or Leninism, Stalinism and Maoism. Each of these not only goes on developing as time passes, but may in its turn split up into further sub-divisions. And each division has quite a lot of canalization, or chreodic character, in the sense that someone who starts off trying to be a heretic, standing midway between Maoism and Leninism perhaps, finds that there are strong pulls trying to drag him into one or other of the orthodoxies.

In such an epigenetic landscape, there are branching points at which a valley splits up into two or possibly more branches. What can one say about them? And what can one say about the question of whether the system as a whole goes down one branch or the other, or breaks up and part goes down each? Take the second question first. Sometimes one knows that there is a branch point ahead of the system, and that if one can give the system a push at the right time, it can be diverted into one or other of the alternatives in front of it. The point to notice here is that it is in general no use giving the push too early: if you do, the system will have got back to the middle of the valley again before it reaches the fork, and the effect of the push will have been dissipated. The period just before the branching point, during which a push will be effective in diverting the system into one or other path, is known in biology as the period of 'competence'. It is no use trying to act on the system to divert it into a particular branch until it has become competent to respond, by going down the valley towards which you have pushed it. Equally, of course, it is not advisable to leave the push until too late. Once the system has started to go down one of the branch valleys, if you still want to divert it into the other you have to push it right over the hill between them. Effective revolutionaries, like Lenin, have been brilliant in choosing just the right time to give a push to a society coming up to a branch point in its stability system.

The question of how the branch points come to be there at all is a difficult one. Remember that the shape of the valley (the slope of the hillsides) represents the net result of a whole lot of controlling actions, each of which is brought about by network effects, or feed-backs of the kind we consider in Chapter 6. Now the strength of these feed-backs and controls would depend on the amounts of the various components present in the system. Therefore, as the system progressively changes as time passes, the strengths of the controls will also alter. As some components of the system increase in magnitude and others contract, controlling interactions which were at first of minor importance may become much more significant, and vice versa. Eventually the system has altered so much that its controls can no longer ensure the stability of the former pathway. It may then break down into a general chaotic turmoil, or it may undergo a branching into two alternative new paths, each with its own stability. It is perhaps rather surprising that so many systems we come across seem to behave in the second way, rather than the first; and I do not know that there is any good explanation yet why this should be so. The theory of such breakdowns of stability is in rather an early stage of development. It is known as catastrophe theory. It seems likely to be one of the most interesting – and quite likely the most important – types of mathematical thought in the near future.

One can again use the idea of an attractor surface to help visualize what is going on. To simplify the model let us forget about providing sloping sides to a valley to represent the canalization of a chreod, but instead indicate this by drawing arrows on the attractor surface, indicating that things get pushed in towards the line representing the pathway of change. We can start with a more or less flat attractor surface, with a line on it, and arrows pointing towards the line. The changes that are going on in the control systems as time passes can be represented by bending the attractor surface. A branch point, or catastrophe, occurs as soon as this bending results in there being a fold which brings one part of the attractor surface vertically under some other part (see 7b.8). Consider then what will happen if a disturbance pushes the system into an abnormal position such as those shown in A or B. The displaced point will first fall back on the attractor surface and then run along the surface to the attractor line. If, at a later time, it gets displaced to A' or B', it all depends whether it falls on the top surface of the fold, when the arrows will push it back into the top chreod; but if it has been displaced to B' it will fall down on to the lower surface, and the arrows on that will bring it into the lower chreod.

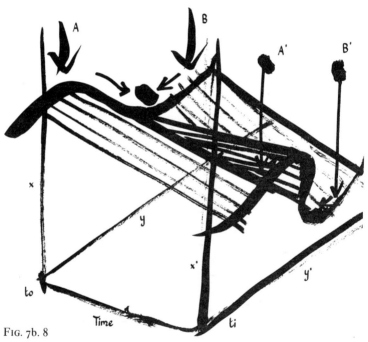

Fig. 7b. 8

Perhaps the visual model gives one some intuitive understanding why systems which reach the limit of their initial stability are often split up into two stable pathways rather than resulting in complete turmoil. The formation of such folds in a surface is the kind of thing one could reasonably expect if the surface had a certain solidarity or strength.

Complete breakdown into chaos would have to be represented by total disruption of the attractor surface, which one might guess was less likely to happen.

*Exploring a Landscape*

An important question about the epigenetic landscape and branching pathways is this: When we are confronted with an unknown system, how do we find out what the shape of the landscape is? In such parts of biology as the study of embryonic development, we can study a large number of individual eggs of the same species, do a lot of experiments on them, and explore their stability by seeing how far they can get back to normality after various sorts of disturbance. In many more important systems, such as those we meet in human and social life, there is only one example of the system, and we cannot use this way of exploring it.

One suggestion, due to the Russian mathematicians Gel'fand and Tsetlin, is to proceed as follows. We find ourselves doing something to a system which we believe has certain stability characteristics, which could be described by an epigenetic landscape; but we have no idea where we are on the landscape when we first start trying to affect the system. So what we should try to do is to alter it, slightly, in as many ways as possible, and observe its reactions. We will find that the system resists some types of change more than others, or restores itself more quickly after changes in some directions than in others. We can think of our actions as going out into the landscape for the same distance in every direction from where we stand, thus describing a circle. But the reactions of the system will be different in different directions, since it will be harder to push the system 'uphill' than 'downhill'. Thus its response will be a distorted circle. From the directions of these distortions, we can deduce the main slope of the part of the epigenetic landscape where we have found ourselves. We then move down this slope – operating in the direction in which the system is most easily altered – taking quite small steps, until we begin to find a mounting resistance: then we immediately withdraw a bit, and are presumably on, or at least very near, the bottom of a valley.

We then remember where we started and from that point take quite a large jump – much bigger than the steps by which we descended the slope – not in the direction of downhill or uphill, or along the contour, where the reactions of the system were equal in response to thrusts of opposite direction, but in some direction intermediate between this contour and the downhill direction. This large jump may perhaps be expected to carry us on to the opposite hillside lower down the valley, and a local exploration around that spot may show us the slope going in the opposite direction. We can again descend this to the valley bottom, and thus trace the course of the valley we are in. That in itself will be quite useful information but, at some point, we have to make another big step, large enough to carry us out of this first valley, over a watershed into one of the other valleys of the landscape, which again we have to explore in the same sort of way.

As Gel'fand and Tsetlin put it, we need by trial and error to fix the length of the long steps so that we 'skirt high hills and step over small watersheds'. One can't, of course, give any general rules for doing this. It has got to be largely a method of 'suck it and see'. A point of general principle is that in exploring such a landscape it would take too long to walk all over it step by step with paces of even length. It is better to alternate between (a) local exploration followed by exploiting the direction of the easiest change, until the change begins to get difficult (i.e. opportunist reformism); and (b) a jump in the dark to try to change some quite different aspect of the situation, followed by another period of opportunist reform around that subject, and keeping in mind a readiness to abandon this attempt if it turns out to be a flop. The procedure is, the Russians suggest, a judicious mixture of mild reforms in one area, followed by letting that area lie, when it ceases to respond, and starting another programme of mild reforms in a quite different context. This, they argue is the best way to get an idea of how the behaviour of the whole system is organized, which is an essential preliminary before one can deal with the whole thing in an effective way.

## C. The Epigenetic Landscape of Human Society

What could one sensibly mean by 'stabilizing' or 'controlling' the human situation in the world of today or tomorrow? The type of behaviour of progressive systems which we have just been discussing – a tendency to lead rather firmly in a smallish number of alternative directions – is found not only in material systems, but in psychological and cultural ones. Christopher Zeeman has used this terminology to describe the way in which many animals seem to switch suddenly between two different types of behaviour, say aggression or fear; it is often some minor factor which decides whether a dog behaves in the 'attack chreod', and bites you, or in the 'frightened chreod', and runs away. Many other students of animal behaviour have described similar phenomena, when it is touch and go whether a male and female fight or mate; though they mostly do not yet use the language of chreods and catastrophes which has been described here, but speak in more particular and less general terms.

In the world of today, many people fear that the situation may be getting out of hand, and soon may run away with itself, and us, into some sort of chaos. Most conventional discussions of 'stabilization' or 'control' of human situations are in terms of simple quantitative measures. For instance, it is pointed out that population numbers, consumption of power, etc., etc., are increasing with time according to an exponential law, so that plotted against time they give a J-shaped curve. It is argued that we need to introduce some negative feed-back control system, which will convert the J-shaped curve into an S-shaped curve.

The first point to note is that at present we are faced with J-shaped curves if we plot against time not just population numbers, power consumption, etc., but their rate of change. We have to deal not with exponential velocities, but with accelerated exponential (see p. 66). We are concerned with the stabilization/control not of things but of processes; with homeorhesis, not homeostasis.

We are also in a phase of increasing diversification or differentiation. Whereas a few decades ago mankind could be classified into blue-collared workers, white-collared workers, professionals and aristocracy or plutocracy, there is now an enormously richer diversity of life-styles and class identifications (if we still use the concept of class). Both these points have been extensively documented by Alvin Toffler in his book, *Future Shock*.

Toffler seems to contemplate both these tendencies continuing more or less unchecked – everything going faster and faster at an accelerating rate, and differentiation between social roles and life-styles becoming ever more diversified, to the point that any one individual will switch styles (including marriage partners, friends, etc.) every few years.

Merely to try to bring these processes to a halt would, in the first place, probably be impossible; and secondly would produce a condition of stagnation and ultimately deterioration. On the other hand, I confess to some sort of (perhaps old-fashioned) intuition that if uncontrolled, they would lead to a situation of total incoherence or turbulence. But what sort of stabilization/control is conceivable? It is not good enough to talk about improving homeorhesis or buffering of particular chreods, since this would eliminate further diversification. It could amount to the authoritarian imposition of uniformity, even if this was imposed by impersonal social forces rather than by an individual dictator like Hitler or Stalin. Diversification demands that the branching of chreods, catastrophes in the sense we discussed above, be allowed to continue. I think what we are concerned with can be loosely put by saying we want to design a system in which the catastrophes are little ones, not big ones. That is to say, when we make a switch in life-style (from a junior advertising executive to a pop group/lyric writer, or from an experimental biologist to a futurologist, philosopher or art critic), people do want the styles to be really *different*, genuinely alternative choices, not just the mixture as before with a trifle more or a trifle less bitters in the cocktail; but surely what we want to aim at is a 'system' which allows us to do this without too much danger of our whole personality being torn into shreds in the process of transition.

One visual illustration would be the very final edge between the land and the sea in a great river delta like those of the Mississippi and the Nile – there are almost innumerable little separate rivulets of the fresh water running down to the sea, separated quite definitely but only by low banks of mud. This would be an 'epigenetic landscape' of low profile. Or one might suggest a musical analogy. We do not want to listen to the confrontation of markedly different themes as in a Wagnerian opera, but to the running through of a gamut of slight variations on one or a few allied themes, as in much of Bach or boogie-woogie.

Or we could put it another way. Using the model of a chreod as an attractor surface in a multi-dimensional space, a catastrophe corresponds to an overlapping fold in this surface (792). The stabilization/control we are looking for corresponds to one in which there are many overlapping folds; but the top and bottom surfaces of the folds are not widely separated; a crumpled surface with many little crumplings, rather than a few large impressive folds.

# 8   Analysing Systems

## A. The Classical Scientific Method

Many of the systems which we understand best, and in particular most of the systems about which our understanding has been increasing most rapidly, are those in which imaginative insight into the structure of the general characters of the processes involved has been reinforced by the application of the scientific method of analysis. This method has proved fantastically powerful in producing both understanding of, and the power to control, nearly every type of system we have come across in the physical and chemical world. Even in such unpromising and messy-looking things as tars and gums and general gunk, chemistry has been able to unravel what they are made of, and how they are put together, and teach us how to make a great variety of plastics, adhesives and so on, which are useful in one way or another. In many – though not yet all – aspects of biological systems, the scientific method has, in the last couple of centuries, and in particular within the last fifty years, produced enormously more understanding of phenomena such as heredity or physiology than man had acquired through all the millenia in which he has been living with his own body, but not trying to understand it in this particular sort of way.

What then is the scientific method? Or one may even ask, is there really any single method of study which is responsible for all the increases of understanding which contribute to science in so many different fields? As a matter of fact, science has by this time become such a general profession that people who are called scientists are as diverse a bunch as those who might be called writers, who range all the way from advertisement copywriters, journalists, pornographers, pop magazine or sci-fi fictioneers, to serious critics, essayists, scholars, novelists, dramatists, poets and indeed scientists. Perhaps workers in science are, after all, not quite such a motley crowd; but many of them hardly ever, if at all, use the rigorous, and usually very difficult method which can be regarded as the classical fully developed method of science. They will, of course, all have been taught it at school or university, just as all writers will have been taught the principles of English grammar and how to construct a decent sentence, but it is at least as rare to come across a scientist who consistently applies the true scientific method as it is to find a writer with an impeccably lucid prose style. So much is this the case that John Platt has suggested that it is confusing to go on referring to the ordinary procedure of scientists as 'the scientific method', which implies that one will find a decent example of it in any scientific paper one likes to open. He suggests that we should characterize the true scientific method more specifically, by naming it 'the method of strong inference'.

The method of strong inference was the invention of the Renaissance. The most famous early description of it, which still remains one of the best, was by Francis Bacon in his book *Novum Organum* (1620). The crux of the method is to make a number of hypotheses as to how things may be working, and then to design an experiment which will give a clear lead whether any of these hypotheses are true or false.

John Platt describes the procedure in more detail as follows:

> Strong inference consists of applying the following steps to a problem in science, formally and explicitly and regularly: (1) devising alternative hypotheses; (2) devising a crucial experiment (or several of them) with alternative possible outcomes, each of which will, as nearly as possible, exclude one or more of the hypotheses; (3) carrying out the experiment so as to get a clean result; and recycling the procedure, making subhypotheses or sequential hypotheses to define the possibilities that remain; and so on.

Notice that John Platt writes of applying these steps to *problems in science*. This is actually not as limiting a condition as it sounds. Science, in fact can be *defined* as all those problems to which this procedure has been successfully applied. If you can apply strong inference to any problem at all, you will have converted that problem into something within the province of science.

This does *not* imply that all efficient questions have to be in terms of physical or chemical entities – atoms, molecules and so on. Mendel's questions, in terms of 'hereditary factors', later referred to as 'genes', were perfectly good science, long before anyone could give a definite physico-chemical meaning to them. By now, of course, we know so much about the physico-chemical make-up of the world that we reasonably expect that most problems can be most profitably formulated in these terms, but that is not essential. There are still some problems, which can be successfully analysed by science which cannot yet be put into simple material terms (e.g. the appearance of patterns during development, or sequences of or actions in animal behaviour).

*Verification, Refutation or Getting a Likeness?*

Notice also that Platt recommends devising experiments which aim at *excluding* one of the alternative hypotheses – proving it wrong and untenable. This is at present the fashionable view about the nature of scientific procedures. Personally, I think that the essential point about a scientific experiment is that it should give a clear yes-or-no answer, and I remain unconvinced that the 'no' answers are more convincing than the 'yes' ones. Several people have argued in favour of 'no' answers, but they have done so for different reasons. Francis Bacon, writing the first description of the scientific method, stated that it 'must analyse nature by proper rejection and exclusions; and then, after a sufficient number of negatives, come to a conclusion on the affirmative instances'. At the time he was writing, empirical and rational science had hardly begun. Man had many beliefs about the nature of the physical world and about living things, but these were deductions from the Holy Scriptures or from classical authors such as Aristotle, not based on observations, let alone on experiments. The first necessity under such circumstances was indeed to debunk the unfounded myths which formed the greater part of accepted wisdom about the nature of the subjects which science had to investigate. Emphasis on rejections and exclusions of the conventional wisdom of the dominant group was very right and proper: things were not, in fact, according to COWDUNG.

For most of the period during which science was developing, from the time of Francis Bacon to about the middle of this century, theorists of science spoke much less of excluding hypotheses. The idea came into fashion again quite recently, for quite a different reason from that which appealed to Bacon. Trying to prove ideas wrong came to the top as a reaction against an over-emphasis on proving them right. In the 1920s, a group of thinkers, mainly centred in Vienna, began a movement which became one of the dominant influences in modern philosophy. Their thesis was that all argumentation and thinking about the world has to treat it as consisting of statements, formulated in some language. Some of these statements are purely logical, but others are supposed to convey information about real affairs. The first group of thinkers of this kind – who are often collectively referred to as 'Linguistic Philosophers' a term which includes not only the early adherents of the idea, but many later developments from them – were a group known as Logical Positivists; they maintained that the meaning of a factual statement was nothing more nor less than the way in which the statement could be verified or proved correct; and if a statement cannot be proved correct by any conceivable procedure, they argued that it had no meaning at all.

It would not be to the point here to pursue the ramifications of this pretty radical philosophical notion, which clears out of the way at one stroke all poetry, metaphysics, rhetoric, commands, metaphor and so on. The relevant point is that these philosophers, who were extremely fashionable throughout the world in the 1930s, demanded *verification*. However, more conventional philosophers, after recovering from the shock of this attack, pulled their logical forces together, and then stated that no one can have 100 per cent verification of any statement, however loud he may call for it. Suppose you have a statement or hypothesis that if p happens q will follow. You do an experiment, in which you produce p, and observe that q does follow. You still have not *proved* the initial statement 'if p then q', because q might have appeared in your experiment not because of the presence of p at all, but as a consequence of some other condition, say k, which you had never thought of, but which you happened to produce at the same time as you produced p. If you make the hypothesis that if you say your prayers tonight, the sun will rise tomorrow; and you say your prayers and it does rise, clearly you have not proved your hypothesis.

But if the verification argument has to be given up, perhaps one can do better with its opposite. Karl Popper pointed out that, given the statement 'If p then q', and you do p and q does *not* follow, then you have disproved the statement; and he argued that the real method of science is not to try to verify statements, but to disprove them. A surprising number of scientists, including very successful ones, have expressed agreement with him. But Popper's argument only holds in the abstract world of pure logic, in which the statement 'If p then q' implies that q will always follow p, whatever all the other circumstances are, so that we are not allowed to bring in some other disturbing factor, like the k in the argument about verification. But the world which science tries to analyse is not the pure world of logic; it is the rough and untidy world of actual happenings. Suppose we have a hypothesis like 'If a match is put to twigs (p) a fire starts (q).' Quite often, when one does this (p), the fire actually does start (q); but as we saw above, one cannot prove the statement absolutely – for one thing one cannot do it often enough. But again, sometimes the fire does not start, the twigs are wet, or something; and this does not completely disprove the suggestion that matches have something to do with starting fires. In the real world of science, one can never have statements which are 100 per cent true in all circumstances or 100 per cent untrue in all circumstances. The mistake made by both sets of philosophers – those who asked for verification and those who would settle for falsification – is that they demand 100 per cent certainty; and that is something we can never have about the real world. All science can do is to show that some things are very likely, others unlikely. Its picture of the world is more like a portrait drawn by a painter than like a precise theorem in logic.

In practice, as far as I can see from the history of scientific discoveries in my own field of biology, and from my own experience, it has sometimes paid off to try to disprove a hypothesis, and at other times to try to prove one. For instance, when Mendel discovered his laws of heredity he was not trying to disprove anything, but was rather trying to verify a hypothesis which he had formulated on the basis that each organism has two parents. Again, Morgan and Bridges used nondisjunction (unusual behaviour of chromosomes) to give *positive* proof that hereditary factors lie in the chromosomes. And Müller discovered that X-rays can induce gene mutations, not to disprove anything, but to confirm his hunch that rays which can penetrate into a cell and change chemical constituents may sometimes change heredities. In my own experimental work, I have sometimes designed an experiment to produce what might be called a disproof. For instance, Spemann discovered a part of an early embryo of the newt, which he called the organization centre, because it induced the formation of the body of the embryo around it; and he supposed that this action depended on its living activities. I thought that it did not, and I proved in an experiment that the centre could produce much the same effect after it had been killed. This could be regarded as an experiment designed to exclude Spemann's hypothesis; but one could equally well describe it as an experiment designed to show the positive fact that the action of the organizer depends on something like a hormone.

The essential point about the effective use of the scientific method is not that you try to prove or disprove hypotheses, which may often be no more than a matter of how do you choose to describe the situation, as in the last instance; it is whether one can discover how to ask important questions, and, in relation to each question, can devise experiments which give clear-cut answers one way or the other. There are, therefore, two different but closely related essential features. Firstly, the questions asked must be of a kind to which clear-cut answers are possible. It is not good enough 'to see what happens' if we raise the temperature, or raise the acidity, or mess about with the conditions in one way or another. One wants questions of the form 'is it *a* or is it *b*?'; and preferably *a* and *b* must be such that the answer should be clearly *a* or *b*, and not 'a bit of both'. But a clear question is no use in itself if there is no available way of answering it. It was no use asking perfectly clear and definite questions about the consistency of the moon's surface until there was some way of sending either a man or a probe up there to obtain the answer. Similarly, there are many questions about history and evolution which can be very definitely stated, but which will probably always remain unanswerable.

It is the ability to formulate clear-cut questions which invite yes-and-no answers, where a technique exists, or can be invented, to obtain these answers, which separates the successful scientist from the merely competent professional. The evidence of the power of the method is all around us, from television, the atom bomb, or the conquest of tuberculosis or malaria to such intellectual triumphs as the theory of evolution or of the atom or of space and time.

## Strong Inference

The argument that the fundamental method of science depends on proving that ideas are wrong, and then rejecting them, tends to reinforce the belief which has been coming into fashion amongst younger people in the last few years that science is a heartless and inhuman affair, and scientists unpleasant characters whom no decent person would wish to resemble. This is such a travesty of the facts that it is worth looking at the situation a bit more closely. Platt refers to the advances in molecular biology as an example of the extraordinary success which can be achieved by consistent and regular application of strong inference. After pointing out that crucial experiments can be found in every field of science he goes on:

The real difference in molecular biology is that formal inductive inference is so systematically practised and taught. On any given morning at the Laboratory of Molecular Biology in Cambridge, England, the blackboards of Francis Crick and Sidney Brenner will commonly be found covered with logical trees. On the top line will be a hot new result just up from the laboratory or just in by letter or rumour. On the next line will be two or three alternative explanations, or a little list of 'what he did wrong'. Underneath will be a series of suggested experiments or controls that can reduce the number of possibilities, and so on. A tree grows during the day as one man or another comes in and argues about why one of the experiments won't work, or how it should be changed.

This is a fair enough account as far as it goes. Certainly Francis Crick and Sidney Brenner are men with a great ability to make cogent criticisms – I have had some of my own ideas given the works in conversation with them often enough to know that – but their great scientific achievements come from something a good deal more important and difficult than just chalking up 'what he did wrong'. The secret is really in those other phrases Platt uses; thinking up 'two or three alternative explanations' and writing down 'a series of suggested experiments'. Crick and Brenner can both see as quickly as anyone alive where an argument breaks down, or needs re-phrasing if it is to hold water. What is more important, they can recognize a new idea when it turns up, or even the germ of one when its originator has not quite mastered it and is developing in the wrong way; and most of the great advances in molecular biology have come not from proving anybody wrong, but from having quite new ideas which have been proved to be right or nearly right. Before Crick and Watson advanced the hypothesis of the double helical structure of DNA, no one had considered the possibility that genetic material might not have a unitary structure, but might be made of two complementary parts. This was a quite novel idea, which led to extraordinary developments. Again, the idea that the proteins whose structure is controlled by the genes are not constructed actually at the site of the genes themselves, but somewhere else in the cell, so that the genes have to pass their instructions to this protein factory by means of a 'messenger', was not just a refutation of some previous notion, but was a novel idea – and Sidney Brenner was deeply involved in thinking it out, and designing and carrying out the experiments which made it seem worthy of acceptance. It could only be with hindsight, and for the purpose of meeting some philosopher's description, that one could with difficulty re-tell the story of the discoveries of molecular biology in terms of refuting hypotheses and rejecting them. The simple way to tell the story is in terms of having ideas, and proving them right by means of experiments which will stand up to the toughest criticism.

So far, I have not said anything about what sort of questions are likely to evoke yes-or-no answers, with the appropriate methods of finding them. Actually, there are probably several different kinds of questions which qualify as potential 'scientific questions'; and people at different periods in the history of science have sometimes been more impressed by one kind, at other times by another. This point has recently been particularly emphasized by the American science-philosopher Thomas Kuhn. In his book *The Structure of Scientific Revolutions* (1962), Kuhn argues that, for most of the time, people, and scientists, see the world through one particular set of spectacles – according to one particular paradigm, as he puts it – and find that questions and answers put in terms of that paradigm are more clear-cut and more definitely yes–no, because they appear with clearer edges through that sort of spectacles. But sometimes, occasionally, and importantly, we put down one set of spectacles and pick up another. We stop thinking of space and time as separate and totally 'obvious', and we start feeling that relativity and space-time gives a deeper insight which we cannot avoid pursuing – even if, as Kuhn claims, at first this new idea solved a few outstanding puzzles only at the expense of throwing away some previously acceptable solutions of others. Or we give up thinking of atoms as indivisible, and attachable to each other only by a few specific 'valencies' – which was the way I was taught chemistry – and we start thinking of atoms as very dynamic centres of activity, definitely divisible, into many different components, and able to combine with one another in several different ways. Or we may even agree to look at one type of process through one set of spectacles for certain purposes and through a quite different set for another; as when we regard light as either continuous waves or discrete particles, or the 'material' physical elements as either 'elementary particles' or 'wave mechanical entities'.

All of this apparent total confusion comes back to the basic points that were made in the first chapter of this book. All our knowledge of the world is based on our experience of it – or, if you insist on professionalizing it, on experiments. And we can never describe in words the *total* content of any experience or experiment. Like a portrait painter, we can capture some aspects of our 'subject' – it is symptomatic of the confusion of philosophical language that the thing the painter refers to as his subject is what the philosophers call the object. And sometimes, we like to see the portrait of nature painted in one style, sometimes in another.

This chapter is about the method of science, rather than about the philosophy of it, so I shall not enter on any full discussion of this Kuhnian view. I shall only remark that it has certainly become very fashionable. But one has to remember that we cannot pick just anything we please as a useful and applicable point of view. The world we live in has a structure, and even though there may be several different ways of looking at it, each providing some insights, they would all have to respect that structure, which is as 'real' as the person whose portrait a painter is doing.

## Hard Work and Skill

The insistence by Kuhn that the direction in which science moves is not dictated only by impersonal logic, but is also a matter of what people find themselves interested in or convinced by, perhaps provides a suitable context in which to mention two points which seem important to most active scientists, but which rarely get mentioned by the professional philosophers of science.

The first is that unearthing the structure of the world we live in is a time-consuming pastime. Talking about 'the scientific method' may give enticing opportunities for brilliant intellectual *recitatives*, duets or cadenzas; actually using the scientific method almost always involves long boring periods of waiting for something to boil, or the eggs to develop to the right stage for the experiment (in my experience, they nearly always insist on doing so at 2.00 am) or finding some way of filling the interval between the first experimental intervention and the next one, which has to be just two and a half hours later. And then, it is not just doing *one* experiment; nothing less than ten, or twenty or even more, repetitions will be at all convincing, particularly when they are difficult to pull off, and only one in half a dozen or more is likely to work at all. The scientific method, for all the philosophical sophistication you like to put into it, involves about as much sheer bloody foot-slogging as sculpture with a chisel against marble.

And that raises the second point. The scientific method, in practice, calls for skill and craftsmanship. This was very obvious in the science with which I started, cutting little pieces (one-third millimetre across) out of one embryo newt or chick and placing them, to fit, into a prepared hole in another embryo. What I first prided myself on, as a scientist, was that I could operate with a precision limited only by the ultimate limitation, that there is a (tiny) pulse at the tip of your forefinger, which gives any instrument you hold a slight jerk every time the heart beats. But even in modern automated super-mechanized experimentation, using instruments designed by the laboratory instrument industry to be sold at fantastic prices, I have watched younger men in the laboratory of which I am Director, setting up experiments which I could not do at all, and I have seen how with X, handling something which is supposed to be automated so it is just a matter of pressing buttons, everything goes perfectly smoothly and it all works as the book says, and every repeat gives an almost identical result, while with Y, poor chap, nothing goes right, he has to try five times before the preparations even begin to look right, and then, when he attempts a repetition, the results come out quite different from the first time. The scientific method, even after the instrument makers have got on to it, still remains a craft skill – which we scientists enjoy but philosophers usually feel to be beneath their notice.

## The Limits of Science

Undoubtedly when confronted with a complex system you will obtain more effective understanding of it if you can apply the scientific method than in any other way. But the fact that science is based on clear answers to specific questions is not only the source of its strength, but also to some extent a limitation. Science does not – not yet, and in some senses, not ever – tell us all about everything. It is a systematization of the answers to those questions which have been successfully put to experimental testing; and not all questions have yet been thought of, and even fewer have been tested in ways which give reasonably clear answers. There are large areas of human concern, particularly problems about man's own nature, and that of his societies, in which it has been very difficult to formulate questions which can be given clear answers in experiments which it is practical or desirable to carry out. In these areas, science is weak; and non-scientific methods of study, relying on hunches, or experience, or intuition, or insight, or empathy or what-have-you, may be the best guide one has available. It can never be as good a guide as scientific knowledge would be. This is chiefly because there is no way for Mr John Smith to judge the rival merits of the insight or wisdom of Statesman X and Prophet Y. It is ultimately an arbitrary choice which he will follow; and although he may try to build on the work of his predecessors, he can never be sure that they provide a firm foundation.

There are two other major difficulties that stand in the way of applying the scientific method of strong inference to each and all the systems we come across. The first is that in many cases we have not yet discovered the right system of concepts in which clear-cut hypotheses can be stated and therefore tested. This is so particularly in systems in which the entities we can most easily identify react with each other in very many complex ways, and seem to behave differently according to the particular context that they are in at a given time.

The method has so far been most successfully applied to systems in which these constituent entities are of not very numerous kinds, and their properties remain more or less constant. There are only a certain number of different kinds of atoms with which chemistry has to deal; the mass and physical dimensions of the bodies about which Newton developed his physics remain the same wherever the bodies were; and there are not many ways in which separate physical bodies can interact with one another. Although the genes and other bodies dealt with by molecular biology are complex built-up things, the properties of the entities remain fixed, or change only in definite ways as the result of a small number of definite processes. These are examples of the kinds of situation in which strong inference works best.

But there are other fields of biology in which the sub-units – or at least the sub-units we normally use at present – do not seem to have such clear-cut properties. We think of the brain as made up of a large number of cells, but it is not at all clear that a particular cell does, or can only do, one or two things. For instance, when quite large parts of the brain are damaged or removed, the remainder may carry out all the functions which the complete brain originally did, and this must involve other cells carrying out the activities which were previously performed by the cells in the part which is destroyed. The scientists working on the functioning of the brain – the neuro-physiologists and others – are no less clever and hard-working than the molecular biologists, but they have made far less spectacular progress; possibly – even probably – this is because they have not yet discovered the right sub-units of the brain's functioning machinery, about which they could ask precise and experimentally answerable questions. Probably it is a mistake to analyse the brain into individual cells; the entities one ought to be asking questions about may be something else – possibly circuits of electric currents, which may retain some important characteristic features whatever particular cells they happen to pass through. One of the points about the discussions in other chapters of this book, about ways in which units can be organized into systems, the kinds of behaviour which systems may exhibit, and the sorts of questions it may be profitable to ask about them, is that these ideas may help us to reach clear-cut and appropriate notions which can be used to ask definite but answerable questions about such things as the brain, or human society, which science has so far not been very successful in tackling.

The other reason, or reasons, why the scientific method of strong inference is not the beginning and ending of wisdom in dealing with complex situations, is that there are some things for which it is not appropriate. In the first place, there are some things about such situations that we may need to measure, and science is not fundamentally concerned with quantities. In view of what one is usually told, this may seem a perverse and paradoxical statement. It is true that many scientists spend much of their time in measuring things, such as the quantities of substance in a compound, or the speed of light, the frequency of a given type of vibration and so on. Some world-famous scientists of the not too distant past – mostly Victorian physicists – claimed that until one had measured something, and turned it into a number, one was dealing only with gossip. But actually science deals not with numbers but with logical relations. It is founded, as we have said, on clear-cut questions which can be given definite yes-or-no answers. These answers may, of course, involve the integers. An atom of iron may be combined with two other atoms, or with three other atoms or conceivably four, five or six or some other integral number; but such relations do not involve numbers like 10·5763 or 21·0274. When a chemist, for instance, measures the amount of oxygen which is combined with a given amount of iron in a certain compound, he does this as the simplest way of discovering which of the various compounds of iron and oxygen he is dealing with, and each of these compounds will involve a few (one, two, three, etc.) atoms of iron, and similar numbers of atoms of oxygen. The measurements only need to be precise enough to make it clear which of these clear-cut alternatives he has got hold of.

However, there are many contexts in which we do have to measure quantities, for practical purposes. These tasks belong really to technology, engineering or agriculture rather than to science itself. The bacteriological scientist may want to know how to distinguish the various forms of germs; but it is the sanitary engineer who needs to measure how many of them there are per millilitre in the town water supply.

One of the first groups of practical people who felt the necessity for developing better methods of measuring quantities in complex situations were the agriculturalists. If you want to test a variety of types of seed, and the effects on them of applying different mixtures of fertilizers, you have a complicated job arranging to get comparable measurements of the final crop which will allow you to evaluate the effects of different combinations of seed and fertilizer treatments. Clearly, for instance, it won't be good enough to have only one plot, with only a certain variety given a certain treatment, because it may be on a patch of bad soil, or exposed to the wind, or in the shade, or something of that kind. Thus the measurement has to be repeated on several similar different plots. How many should there be, and how should they be arranged and so on? This is all an elaborate development of the methods of statistics; and this particular branch of the subject became known as the 'Design of Experiments'.

I remember the time in the 1930s when the subject became highly fashionable, and Chairs of it were established in some of the oldest and most orthodox universities. At about that time, I went to visit and get some advice from Professor David Keilin, the famous biochemist, a Polish refugee in Britain, who discovered many of the major enzymes concerned with oxidation in biological systems. After dealing with the immediate business in hand, he asked me how I was getting on with the biological research which I was only just beginning. I said I had done the first experiment which had gone quite well, but I was having difficulty in thinking just what to do next. I wondered whether I should do some reading in this new study, the 'Design of Experiments'. Keilin's very soft and gentle voice rose several tones in horror. 'My young friend,' he said, 'there is only one principle in designing experiments; the rest is statistics, leave that to the engineers. If one of my experiments cannot be interpreted without statistics, I leave it and think of a better experiment.' And he turned away, as though the conversation was finished. 'Well, yes, Keilin,' I said, 'but what is the one principle of designing experiments?' He turned back. 'The one principle, my friend, is to design them so that they give an answer.'

So, if you have to understand a complex system in a way suitable for carrying out operations on it of a technological or engineering kind, then you may have to measure various aspects of it as accurately as you can, and you may have to rely on statistics; but this will not be science, and the methods of strong inference will not be applicable.

Finally, of course, one may want to deal with a system in a way which is neither scientific nor technological, but, say, aesthetic, ethical or religious. There are large and very important types of experience for which language itself is inappropriate, let alone strong inference – music, painting, poetry, dance and drama. These modes of being have their own procedures and methods, but I shall not attempt to describe them or discuss them in this book.

# B. Statistics

Statistics is obviously one of the important ways of analysing complex systems. In fact, some people, when reading the title of this book, may expect to find it mainly about statistics. However, statistics is only one of the Tools for Thought, and a very tricky one to use.

Statistics is the name for a number of methods of analysis which are appropriate to use when one is studying, not a single individual thing, but a population of similar things. This is actually the case more often than one might think at first sight. Obviously, if one is interested in something like the birth-rate in India, or the number of Frenchmen who own TV sets, or traffic accidents, one will have to deal with populations containing many individual examples, and will have to find some way of taking account of the differences between them as well as the similarities. But even when one might hope one could concentrate on a single thing, it often turns out that one cannot. This is particularly so if one wants to measure anything. What does this suitcase weigh? Well, you weigh it. But how sensitive is your balance? Unless you have some other knowledge of its accuracy, all you can do is to weigh the suitcase again, and see if you get the same answer. You are now dealing with a population of weight-measurements (with so far only two members). But if you are trying to be accurate, you will almost certainly find that if you weigh it a second time you get a result which is nearly but not quite the same as the first. You may be content to accept the weight which is repeated every time as accurate enough; but you can go a bit further if you will weigh it several times, and provide yourself with a 'population of weight-measurements' with a fair number of members.

Statistics contains a few general ideas about populations which are important enough to be worth everybody's while to understand. They are probably easier to grasp from visual diagrams than from words or mathematical symbols. But words and symbols have to be used to deal with the other part of statistics, which is a set of rules about the arithmetic necessary to handle measurements or counts made on populations. These statistical procedures are quite difficult to understand correctly, and are tricky to use. Fortunately they are rarely called for in ordinary life, because in situations in which it may be important to measure some fact about a population – say, the frequency of accidents on different types of roads – the cost of putting into operation any new knowledge that might emerge, e.g. by improving certain roads, are usually so large that it would not be sensible to undertake it unless the differences are so great that they leap to the eye without any need for elaborate statistical arithmetic. But if, for your purposes, you need detailed and accurate estimates based on statistics, *call in an expert statistician*; this is a Tool for Thought which can only be used precisely after training.

## Populations

Statistics starts with a set of measurements on the individuals in a population; as an example, the heights in inches of the children in a school. One can't do much with them, of course, until they have been put into some sort of order. The first step is to arrange them into groups, bringing together all the measurements which fall between certain limits. We might make the limits two inches apart (or any other interval suitable for the purpose we have in mind). If we take two-inch intervals, then we put together all the measurements between, say, 4 ft (14 cm) and 4 ft 2 in. (19 cm) (48 and 50 in.), and between 50 and 52 ins (19 and 24 cm), 52 and 54 ins (24 and 29 cm), etc., all the way up to the largest measurement we have. Then we count the numbers in each group; and we call the number of measurements in the group between, say, 54 and 56, the *frequency* of measurements in that interval. So we have a table of frequencies, something like the table 4b.1; or we can make a diagram in which we plot the frequency of measurements in each interval. This gives us a stepped outline; and we can, to make things prettier (and more easy to handle mathematically), draw a smooth curve which removes the jaggedness. The type of graph which gives a stepped outline is known as a *histogram*, and the smooth curve is a *frequency curve* (8b.1).

As I have said, there is an elaborate mathematics of statistics. This provides a formula which fixes the shape of a 'normal' frequency curve. By 'normal', it means the frequency of variant types of individuals in a population when those variations are produced by pure chance. If you now persist in asking, what do you mean by 'pure chance', the answer is not at all easy, and there are several schools of thought about how chance is best defined. But for all practical purposes, one can answer that we say something is the result of chance when we believe that it is affected by such a large number of factors, each with only slight effects, that it would be hopeless to try to discover exactly what combination of circumstances had brought about the result we observe. (The word 'random' is often used in the same sense as 'chance'.)

This 'normal frequency curve of chance variations' is highest for middle values, and tails off towards each extreme. It is often described

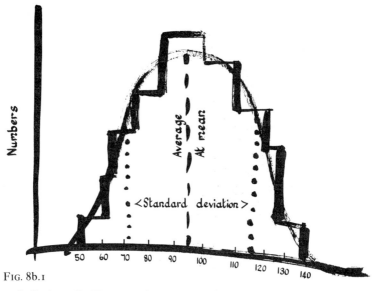

Numbers

Average

At mean

<Standard deviation>

50  60  70  80  90  100  110  120  130  140

FIG. 8b.1

as 'bell-shaped'. The most important properties of any actual example of such a curve, which describes the frequency distribution of variants in some real population, can be characterized by two numbers. The first states the position of the mid-point of the curve; this is the average measurement, otherwise known as the mean. The second describes how widely the measurements are scattered around the mean. There are a number of possible ways of describing this. One might simply calculate how much each individual measurement differs from the mean, or average, and then take the mean of these differences. Statisticians, who seem very conscious of the value of jargon in adding an air of profundity to simple ideas, usually speak of the measurements *deviating* from the mean, so this calculation would give the 'mean deviation from the mean'. But this simple measure turns out to have awkward mathematical properties. One gets an index of scatter which is more easily handled if one deals with the mean of the squares of the deviations. This is a much-used index – the mean squared deviation from the mean, often called the 'variance'. But although this has useful properties when it comes to more elaborate arithmetic, it gives rather a false impression at first sight, because we are not used to having to deal simultaneously with both an ordinary number, in the mean, and a squared number, in the index of scatter. So it has become conventional to quote the index of scatter as the square root of the mean squared deviation. This is known as the 'standard deviation'. It gives an immediately graspable idea of the variability or scatter of the measurements. For instance, if we measured the milk yield of a herd of cows, we might find that its mean was 900 gallons. The variability, expressed as variance, or mean squared deviation, might be 22,500 square gallons – and it is not very easy to gather much impression from that, unless you are used to this sort of game. But the same variability, expressed as 'standard deviation', would be the square root of that, i.e. 150 gallons. This sounds much easier to understand. To get some definite idea from it, all we need to know is what the standard deviation corresponds to in terms of numbers of measurements. This has been worked out in detail. Actually just over two thirds of all measurements will fall between one standard deviation below and one above the mean, i.e. between 750 and 1,050 gallons, while just over 95 per cent will be within two standard deviations on either side of the mean.

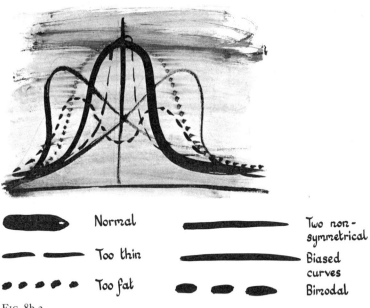

| Normal | Two non-symmetrical |
| Too thin | Biased curves |
| Too fat | Bimodal |

FIG. 8b.2

Of course, not all populations have their variants 'normally distributed', in the manner just described (8b.2). The frequency curve may have a shape which is 'too fat', or 'too thin', in comparison with the normal curve. Or it may be asymmetrical; then the most frequent type is not exactly the same as the average, or mean, and is given the technical name of the 'mode' (or modal type). Sometimes, the population may have two, or even more, very common types, when the population is called 'bi-modal', or 'multi-modal'. These deviations from normality arise usually because the causes producing the variations do not completely fulfil the definition we gave of randomness, i.e. of being so numerous and each of such slight effect that they cannot in practice be separated. Non-normal distributions are usually a sign that the population is being affected by a few factors which are considerably more effective than all the others. The kind of non-normality may give hints how to identify these factors, but this becomes a very technical job which we shall not pursue here.

*Samples*

So far this account has implicitly assumed that one could measure every individual in the population being studied. In practice this is often not the case. It should be possible to take the height of every girl at Ronald Searle's famous St Trinian's, although, if we believe what we read about that school, there might be practical difficulties even there. One could certainly not expect to measure the height of everyone in London or New York; in fact one couldn't even determine exactly who *are* everyone in London or New York, because they are changing all the time, although one can attach a meaning which is definite enough to be useful to the expression 'the population of New York'. What one has to do in such cases is to take a *sample* of the population (8b.3). A good deal of the most practically important statistical ideas are concerned with the theory of sampling.

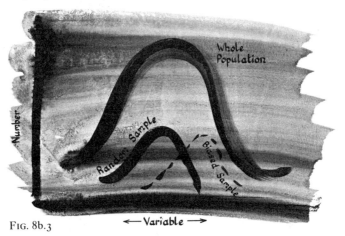

FIG. 8b.3    ← Variable →

The first thing to realize is that a sample cannot be expected to provide a completely accurate representation of the whole population.

This will be true even if it is a 'fair' sample; that is, say, one in which any individual is as likely as any other to be included. Clearly you will not get a good picture of the heights of the girls of St Trinian's, if you measure only a quarter of them, and choose the tallest ones you can see. It is often necessary to take great care to see that the sample being used is an unbiassed one – a 'random' sample, it is often called. This is one of the questions it pays to ask, when someone is trying to persuade you of some statistical argument; is he using a truly random sample? If that point is all right, then it is obvious the accuracy will increase if we make the sample larger, i.e. nearer to taking in the complete population. But in practical terms the question we are likely to be interested in is either, how accurate a picture can we expect from the sample we have been able to get hold of, or, how large a sample will we have to take to attain a certain degree of accuracy?

The best way to understand how these problems have been approached is to do a 'think-experiment' (8b.4). Suppose you took one sample, say, of *n* individuals, and worked out an estimate of the population average and standard deviations from that; and then took another similar sample, and another, and another, and worked out estimates from them also. You would now have a population of estimates. This would have an average of all the estimates of the average, and also have a standard deviation of that 'average of averages' (which has to be arrived at by a slightly different formula; but we need not go into that refinement here). As before, any particular estimate of the average derived

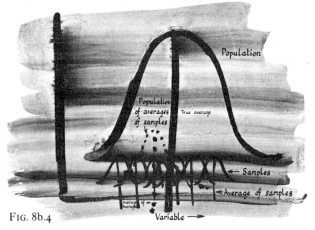

FIG. 8b.4

from one sample will fall more than one deviation away from the true average in only about a third of cases, and more than two deviations away in less than one case in twenty. In this way, one can work out how reliable the picture given by one sample should be considered to be. Unfortunately, there cannot be a simple rule saying how many individuals there should be to make a reliable sample, because this must depend on how much variation there is between the individuals, as well as on their number. But an average based on a sample should always be given as a number followed by an estimate of its reliability, which is normally written as plus-or-minus another number which gives what I referred to above as the estimate of the 'standard deviation of the average of averages' – which is more conventionally called 'the standard error' of the estimated average.

The point of describing this rather murky and technical piece of argument is not that everybody needs to follow every step in the argument. They don't; I have already said that the sensible things to do with statistics is either to become an expert at them, or just skim off the basic ideas. And the basic idea here is that an average, or an estimate of anything else, is very little use unless one has some idea of how reliable it is. Distrust any figures quoted to you, without any indication of their reliability.

Of course, if they are based on measuring something in a complete population, they will not suffer the statistical uncertainties; but they may suffer others. For instance, consider a figure like the numbers of unemployed; they are based on a total count of all those registered in some official way or other as unemployed; but, perhaps particularly in connection with women, one may doubt whether being unemployed is quite the same thing as being registered as unemployed. The uncertainty here is one of the definitions used.

Again, consider the number of people killed in car accidents on a Bank Holiday week-end; it should be possible to get a reasonably accurate total count, though a few may die later from longer-term consequences. But usually such figures are wanted in connection with arguments about whether the roads are getting safer or more dangerous. So one is wanting to compare one year with another. And, of course, the first uncertainty is that maybe more people got killed this year than last because more people were out, or were going farther; because car ownership had gone up; or the weather was better; or what have you. So one wants figures of 'deaths per mile' (or possibly 'deaths per hour of road use'?; it is not absolutely easy to be sure which would be more informative). If these uncertainties were overcome reasonably satisfactorily, we are approaching the problem area which is statistics' own back garden. Suppose the holiday week-end death rate was only forty-eight per million miles this year, while it was fifty-three last year. How much comfort can we take in this apparent 10 per cent reduction? Actually one can have no idea whether it means anything of long-lasting significance (it's obviously good at the time), until it can be fitted into some sort of population of measurements. What was it the year before last, and the year before that and so on? We want a population of death rates, from which we can work out a measure of variation, and then we can see whether this particular measurement, this year, is likely to belong to the same population, or looks rather as though it does not fit in with the earlier ones, which would indicate that some real change had occurred in the general situation (8b.5).

Of course, estimates which are definitely based on samples should be easier to 'place' in this respect, because they *should* (and my advice is to

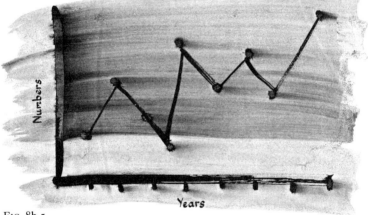

Fig. 8b.5

insist on this) come with an estimate of their 'probable error'. As a *very* rough rule of thumb, one can say that if we are presented with two estimates of something, each with their probable error (say, the averages, over the same five-year period, of the percentage of students entering the Faculties of Science in two universities, who graduated B.Sc. in the minimum prescribed period), and if we ask, do these figures suggest that the two universities have different standards or practices, we should look at the difference between the averages, and if this is less than twice the larger of the two probable errors, we can conclude that there is not much chance (only about one in twenty, or 5 per cent) that there is any difference between them in this connection. Note a point here: what most statistics is about – and the most rewarding question to be asking yourself – is very often of the form: are these two things different? And that, of course, will lead on to: if so, why so?

The only general principle about assessing the reliability of measurements or estimates is that they can never be 100 per cent reliable. All that the most elaborate statistics can do is give you something like betting odds for or against the hypothesis that something is so, or is not so; and it leaves you to decide whether to bet, and how much to put on. One can usually get a good enough idea of the odds intuitively, if one can present the data in a form in which one's intuition can get to work on them. For most people, a visual presentation is easier to grasp than a numerical one.

*Correlations*

Another important part of statistics is concerned with finding out how closely two different sets of things are connected with each other, or, as the jargon has it, are 'correlated'. Here again a simple diagram will probably make it easy to deduce anything that is worth knowing for practical purposes. Make a graph, plotting one thing against the other – say, height vertically and weight horizontally (8b.6). Probably one will find that, in the population you are studying, the taller people are on the whole heavier. It may be possible to draw a straight line, sloping upwards to the right around which all the points are grouped. This line expresses the correlation between the two variables, and its slope is called the correlation coefficient. There are elaborate mathematical techniques for doing this as accurately as possible, but doing it by eye is likely to be good enough in most cases.

Moreover, looking at a graph makes it easy to see some of the snags that may arise. In the graph 8b.7, if you just put the figures through an arithmetical mill, without carefully thinking about them, you might come out with a strong relation between the two variables, such as indicated by the dashed line. But looking at the drawing one immediately sees that this is mainly dependent on the two most extreme measurements, indicated by crosses. Anything dependent on only two measurements is not likely to be very reliable. If the largest and smallest measurements were neglected, there would be no very strong evidence of a correlation between the variables over the rest of their range of variation; one could draw a number of dashed lines, all equally plausible

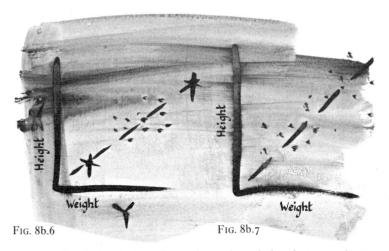

FIG. 8b.6                              FIG. 8b.7

and equally unconvincing. Or perhaps the relation between the two things is not to be represented by a straight line at all, but should be in the form of a curve; and if so, the mathematical techniques for finding the curve are very clumsy and troublesome, little better than doing it by eye.

It is important to realize what a correlation between two variables means, and in particular, what it does *not* mean. It means that, in the population studied (*not* necessarily in all populations), there is a tendency, whose strength is expressed in the correlation coefficient, for the measurements of the two correlated characteristics on the same individual (say, its height and weight) to vary together; the more one measurement departs from the average, the more the other will do so too. This does *not* mean that one characteristic causes the other; it may do so, but the fact that they are correlated is not good enough evidence to reach that conclusion. They can both be caused by something else, and have no essential causal relation to each other. This is a very basic point of warning about the misuse of statistics. It is usually enshrined in an old parable, known as the 'Top Hat Fallacy' – and the fact that it is out of date sartorially should not make you forget that it is still bang-on in what it implies. I quote it in the words of a former President of the Royal Society, in his memorandum about how to do operational research: 'Statistical investigation of the population of many cities would show that the wearers of top hats are significantly taller than the average. The missing causally effective variable here is clearly the higher average income of the top-hat-wearing group.'

# 9  Communication in Systems

## A. Information Theory

Much of the discussion in earlier chapters has been concerned with subjects like structures or organized systems of control. These are not material things. Most of the rest of this book will move even more definitely out of old-fashioned materialism into the realm of ideas and concepts. One of the most influential strands in recent thinking about the complexities of the world we live in has been the idea that the specific character of things may sometimes be more important than the chemical nature of the substances they are made of or their physical properties of mass, acceleration, position and so on. In a rather primitive form, this is an old idea in biology, where the difference between a cat and a dog is not so much a matter of their chemical construction, let alone their physical size, weight or position in space, but depends on their characteristic forms and behaviours. When this sort of notion is broadened to apply to the world in general, including non-living parts of it, and when it is defined more precisely, the concept of 'specific character' has usually been translated into the term 'information'. This word has been given a very definite meaning in a body of thought known as 'Information Theory', and when it is used in anything other than casual conversation, it should be used in accordance with that definition, so it is as well to know what that is. Unfortunately, as we shall see, the definition, although precise, is also very limiting, and excludes most of what we are really interested in. The world does not work by 'Information'; when it operates in any way, it does so by 'instruction' or 'programs', which involve something more than can be accommodated within 'Information'.

Although one or two mathematicians and theoretical physicists had hinted at such a development rather earlier, the formal theory of information is mainly based on the work of a communications engineer at the Bell Telephone Laboratories, Claud Shannon, who was soon joined by a mathematician, Warren Weaver. Shannon and Weaver took as their starting point the idea of something which gives out a message, and something which receives it. But those two items alone do not make up the whole of an effective system. We really need four items, and there is a fifth which we cannot avoid. As well as the 'Information Source', which originates a message, we need a transmitter, which first translates the message into the form of signal which can be transmitted ('codes' it, e.g. from letters into the dot-dash Morse code) and then transmits it along some channel, such as a wire or by radio waves; then there has to be a receiver, which accepts the message and decodes it back into a form understandable by the fourth item, the destination. And the fifth, unwanted but unavoidable, item is a series of activities which tend to disrupt, or distort or otherwise interfere with the message during its transmission. All these disturbing influences are referred to as noise.

For Shannon, the communications engineer, the crucial problem was: how far is the message received by its final destination a faithful rendering of the message as it was originated by its source? He proposed to study this by measuring the amount of 'information' contained in the originated message, and comparing it with the amount of identical information in the message at its destination. But, how to measure 'amount of information'? Let us, to make it simpler, forget about transmitters having to code the message, and receivers decode it, and suppose that we are dealing with messages written in a sequence of letters of the English alphabet, and that the transmitter has a way of sending these down the transmission channel at a rate which the channel has capacity enough to handle without loss or distortion, and the receiver a way of picking them up at the other end. Suppose we have a message, CAT. For the first letter, there are twenty-six letters available in the alphabet; and we have to *choose* one of them, namely C, and so for the second, third, etc., letters of the message, we have to choose one particular letter out of a possible set of twenty-six. The *amount of information*, Shannon argued, can be measured as the *amount of choice*.

And here note a first, and very important, limitation on the generality of the theory. It deals with *choice out of a defined set of possibles*. If we were dealing with the Russian alphabet, with thirty-one letters, choosing the $c$ involves *more* choice, thus more information, than choosing $c$ from the English alphabet with only twenty-six letters. Formal Information Theory can only be applied within a defined universe of possibilities, whose boundaries are known. Most of the world is not like that.

Pursuing his line of thought, Shannon pointed out that in the English language, some letters occur much more often than others: $e$ is more frequent than $q$ or $x$, for instance. So if you exerted no choice about the next letter to go into your message, but left it to chance, it would be more likely to turn out to be an $e$ than a $q$. When he took this into account, and worked out a method of estimating how much choice is really involved in writing down one sequence of letters rather than another, he came up with a certain algebraic formula. The argument is not very difficult to anyone with the rudiments of a mathematical training, but as this book is addressed to people who do not have, and may be allergic to, even the rudiments of mathematics, I shall not give it here (see Shannon's own paper, 1962).

Shannon measured information in units called 'bits'; and one can define a 'bit', well enough for our purposes, as the information involved in giving the answer to a single question whose answer can only be either yes or no. The important point is that Shannon found that the formula for estimating the number of bits in a complex piece of information is identical with one of the most important formulas in the physical sciences, that which embodies the Second Law of Thermodynamics. This Second Law is, C. P. Snow claimed, the shibboleth by which one can distinguish the Two Cultures; members of the Scientific Culture know what it means, members of the Non-Scientific (Humanities? Arts?) Culture do not. It is because Shannon's Information Theory ran straight into the famous Second Law that people thought it must be basically important at a very fundamental level.

So we have to look at the Second Law. It is simple common sense; and no one would have the slightest difficulty about it, except that, unfortunately, the official way of expressing it strikes most people as being upside down. What it states is that, usually and except in special circumstances, any orderliness there may be in a situation tends to get less. If you start by setting up some well-drilled troops into an orderly square, with all the rows strictly lined up by the right, and the files precisely one behind the other, and leave them there for a few hours, you will almost inevitably find that at the end of the period the rows are not so neat and the files are a bit wriggly on the ground. There is nothing unexpected in that. It probably is fair to say that this type of behaviour is one of the most basic and fundamental characteristics of the physical world. Nobody would have much difficulty in understanding it, and accepting it, except that the physicists have chosen to express it in a way which seems to flout our intuition. Most people seem to have a feeling that order is positive, and when it breaks down and becomes dissipated, something is reduced. Physical theory puts it the other way round. It has a word, not for order, but for disorder, which it calls *entropy*; and it expresses the Second Law by saying that *entropy tends to increase*, instead of saying that order tends to decrease.

This turning of the natural way of things upside down is a fairly trivial matter, which anyone with a few wits at his disposal could take in his stride. But when we start to look into its connection with Information Theory, the confusion gets worse confounded.

Information Theory, as Shannon developed it, came out with an algebraic expression which clearly meant it had to have some link with the Second Law and entropy. But what link? Shannon at first thought one way; then he – or was it Warren Weaver? – thought another, almost the exact opposite.

Shannon started by asking himself, how much information can the Information Source put out? Clearly, if all it could do is something totally orderly, like saying A A A A . . . indefinitely, or running through its A B C . . . and when it got to Z starting again, then it could not be the source for many different messages. He therefore at first argued that the 'information capacity' of a source is measured by the degree to which it is *not* orderly; that is to say, by its entropy; the more entropy, the more information.

But then there were second thoughts. What we are really interested in is not so much, how many different messages can the source produce, but rather, how much information is there in *this* message which we are trying now to get through to its destination? Now if the source was in a state of high entropy, or disorder, the message would just emerge as a random sequence of letters, each successive letter chosen by the throw of a dice – which might be biassed to correspond to the average frequency of the letter in normal English, so that *e* turned up more often than *q*. But the information contained in any particular message can only be dependent on the degree to which the sequence of letters spelling it out is *not* determined by chance, but actually spells something. So the amount of information is the degree of choice, not chance; the degree of order, not of disorder. In fact, the more information, the *less* entropy; the precise negative of the previous conclusion.

It is this second view that has become fashionable. So much the vogue indeed, that a special word has been coined to mean 'entropy with a minus sign in front of it', which is called 'negentropy'. This can, roughly but adequately for our purposes, be interpreted as 'order'. And since living systems (including societies) tend to be rather orderly as things go in the world in general, and tend to incorporate anything they take up into the orderliness of their existing structures, you will frequently come across, from people who want to exhibit their mastery of with-it jargon, phrases like 'Life lives on negentropy', and the like.

I hope I have expounded the situation enough for you to see the reasons for my advice: BE ON YOUR GUARD!

The genuine importance of Information Theory is that it brought home the crucial point that there is more to the world than the physical factors of position, mass, acceleration and so on, or the chemical factors of atomic and molecular composition. It pointed out that there is another realm of fundamentally important factors, which we might, non-committally, call 'specificity of character'. Its weakness is that it tried to define this specificity in essentially non-active terms. To quote Warren Weaver's classical paper (1962, p. 116): 'An engineering communication theory is just like a very proper and discreet girl accepting your telegram. She pays no attention to the meaning, whether it is sad, or joyous or embarrassing. But she must be prepared to deal with all that comes to her desk.'

If your telegram reads MEET HIGH MARKET TWELVE TEN, or instead is MEAT HIGH MARKET TWELVE TON, for Information Theory the difference rests *only* in the letters third from the beginning and second from the end. It measures this difference in terms of the likelihood that a throw of dice would put an E or an A in the first place, or an E or an O in the latter. The fact that the first is an arrangement for a meeting at the junction of High St and Market St, and the second a message from a meat importer to a wholesaler that he had better unload twelve tons of doubtful stuff as soon as possible, is nothing whatever to do with the Theory – it falls right outside its province, and is not, and cannot be, measured by it. But of course, it is just this *meaning* which is the real point, both to us as conscious actors in the world, and to all living things carrying on their business of living, whether they are conscious or not.

In Information Theory, once a message containing a certain quantity of information has been given out by the source, the only change in that quantity can be a reduction, by something getting lost or swamped by noise. In particular, the quantity of information cannot increase, until the source gives out some more. This is another of the features of the theory which make it inappropriate to most contexts involving living things. A fertilized egg, for instance, obviously gets more complex (and thus comes to contain more information) as it develops. In a society, a simple small amount of information – a declaration of war, for instance – may gradually produce very far-reaching changes which would need a great deal of 'Information' to describe. This is because systems like living organisms or societies are, in most of their activities, operating not on a basis of information, but of instructions. They do indeed depend on 'specificity', as Information Theory emphasized; but not specificity defined as meaningless 'information' (or negentropy); but rather specificity which is in the form of instructions, or program for action (or 'algorithms', if you must have an impressive-sounding jargon word). Unfortunately, the Theory of Instruction is far less fully worked out and watertight than the Theory of Information, as we shall find out in the next section. It seems always to be easier to make a Good Theory of something which is beside the point and boring than of anything which goes to the heart of the matter. The world may be a plateful of oysters, but it is only the empty oysters which open at all easily.

## B. Instructions and Programs*

One gets a better idea of the real nature of the complex systems we actually come across if one thinks of them, not in static terms of the amount of information they contain, but by asking the more dynamic question, how much instruction was necessary to produce them, or what instructions do they tend to impose on their surroundings? The Theory of Instructions, and of the results of sets of several instructions, which are known as 'programs', is much more difficult and less well understood than that of Information. One soon gets involved with the whole problem of programming to computers. This is easy enough to do when it is only a question of telling the computer to carry out some simple task, perhaps in arithmetic; it is much more difficult to discover the best way to give more complex instructions; and no one can yet foretell all the consequences of an untried program of instructions. This book is not concerned with the technical details of such things as computer programming.

However, to look at something in terms of instructions instead of information usually gives a very different, and often very surprising picture of it. One way to illustrate this is to consider the complexities, both of pattern and behaviour, which can result from very simple instruc-

* Note that, in this context, this is not just an American spelling of a word which, in English, is written 'programme'. The word 'program' has been adopted as a technical term in the language of computer science and related topics, to refer to an organized sequence of instructions.

tions which are carried out over and over again. Some of the simplest examples are patterns which can be produced on a chequerboard of squares. The following game is one instance. A square may be empty or shaded or black. Its state depends on the four squares which share a side with it. The instructions are: (a) an empty square which adjoins one, but only one, side of a full (shaded or black) square becomes black ('a new individual is born'); (b) all the new black squares in a pattern appear simultaneously (making a 'move' in the game); (c) in the next move after it is black, a square remains full but becomes shaded, and in the following move it becomes empty again. The first four moves, starting from a single square, are shown below, and the drawing at the bottom (9b.1) shows the complex but orderly pattern which appears at the forty-fifth move.

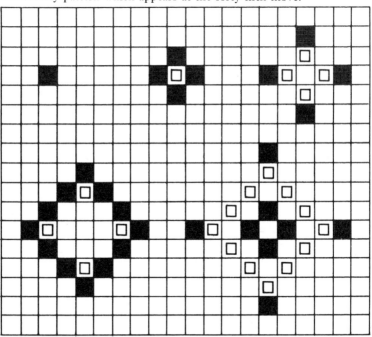

Fig. 9b.1

It is not too surprising, when one thinks about it, that the application of simple rules can produce results of great complexity, as we have just seen. It is perhaps more unexpected to find that rules which seem to take into account only local circumstances can give results which show an overall, and not merely local, orderliness. Here is a very simple example. String together in a line the three letters *a*, *b* and *c*. The rule for adding a new letter at the end of the line is: compare the last letter and the last letter but one (in the string *abbcba*, these would be *a* and *c*); if they are different (as here) add the other letter, i.e. *b*; if they are the same repeat that letter (i.e. in *bab* add another *b*).

You will find that if you start with any group of three letters (except the repetitions *aaa*, *bbb* and *ccc*, which go on indefinitely), you will come to one or another of three sequences of eight letters, *aabcbbac*, *aacbccab* or *bbcaccba*, which will then go on being repeated indefinitely. If you make a mistake, putting down a *c* where you should have put a *b*, all that will happen is that you switch from one of these sequences to another.

One can get equally unexpected results of stability, or the production of specific end-results, from the games on chequerboards. Suppose we allow the squares to have only two states: black (full) or white (empty); suppose that again they pay attention only to the four squares along their sides; then give the instructions (a) a cell with an even number (0, 2 or 4) of black neighbours itself becomes or remains white, (b) a cell with an odd number of black neighbours (1 or 3) becomes or remains black. Then one gets such a surprising result as that shown in 9b.2, in which a pattern of three spots produces four repeats of itself at the second move and as many as sixteen at the sixth.

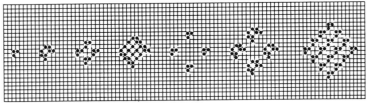

Fig. 9b.2

*The Same Rules and Different Starts*

Probably the most astonishing results in such a game of instructions have been produced by a set of rules proposed by the Cambridge mathematician, J. H. Conway (for a game which he calls 'life', and it seems to justify the title). In this the squares are again either black or white, but they pay attention to all eight squares which touch them, including those at the corners. The instructions are (a) every black square which has two or three black neighbours remains black ('survival'); every black square with four or more black neighbours becomes white ('dies of overcrowding'); (b) every black square with only one or no black neighbour becomes white ('dies of isolation'); (c) any white cell which has three, no more and no less, black neighbours becomes black ('a birth').

Nothing very exciting happens if one starts off from a set of three adjoining blacks; of the five possible starting patterns, three die out immediately, and the other two stabilize as an inactive block or an oscillation with period two (9b.3).

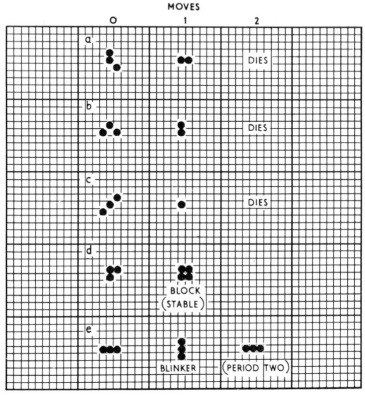

Fig. 9b.3

Things are not much more exciting if one begins with four blacks, although one pattern develops for some time before it settles down to oscillate between two more elaborate arrangements in the last two drawings in the row (9b.4).

It is when we start with five blacks that we come to realize how characterful and unexpected the results of these simple instructions can be. For instance, one pattern produces a 'glider', which, in four moves, shifts itself one column of squares over to the right, and goes on doing so indefinitely (9b.5). Another quite simple group of five (9b.6) undergoes extraordinary developments. Its fate is not yet known. Conway has

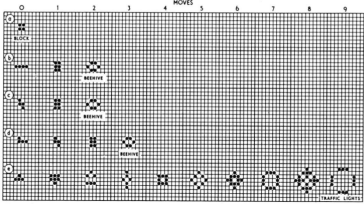

FIG. 9b.4

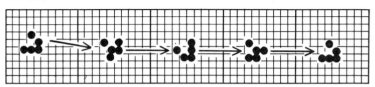

FIG. 9b.5

FIG. 9b.6

tracked it for 460 moves. By then it has thrown off a number of gliders. Conway remarks:

> It has left a lot of miscellaneous junk stagnating around, and has only a few small active regions, so it is not at all obvious that it will continue indefinitely. After 48 moves it has become a figure of seven counters on the left and two symmetric regions on the right which, if undisturbed, would grow into a honey farm (four beehives) and traffic lights. However, the honey farm gets eaten into pretty quickly and the four blinkers forming the traffic lights disappear one by one into the rest of a rather blotchy population.

For long-lived populations such as this one Conway sometimes uses a PDP7 computer with a screen on which he can observe the changes. The program was written by M. J. T. Guy and S. R. Bourne. Without its help some discoveries about the game would have been difficult to make.

More complex starting arrangements produce even more bizarre results. At the top left in 9b.7 is a 'glider gun' of forty-six blacks, which

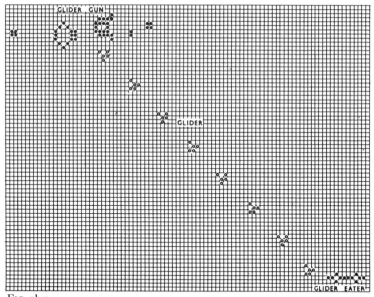

FIG. 9b.7

throws off a new glider every thirty moves, while at the bottom right is an arrangement which 'eats' gliders.

These games illustrate the unexpectedness of the behaviour which can arise when systems follow quite simple instructions. They are a warning that there are a lot of things in the world to which one cannot apply the Information Theory argument which supposes that if we start with a certain quantity of information, which measures the amount of detail there is in the system, the only thing that can happen in the natural course of events is that some of this gets lost. On the contrary, if we start with simple instructions, the amount of detail may not only increase indefinitely in some cases, but it may become arranged in very orderly ways. Unfortunately, one cannot do much more than illustrate this point, because very little definite theory has been worked out about it.

*Different Rules and the Same Start*

This game of 'life' gives some pretty examples of the complexities of shape and behaviour which can arise from following a few simple instructions, and the enormous variety which can be engendered simply by starting from different, though all quite simple, initial configurations. It is worth glancing at the different results which can come about starting always from the same, simplest possible beginning, a single point, but following slightly different, but again simple, programs of instructions.

This game, generally known as 'worms', seems to have originated when one of the better-known researchers on the possible 'intelligent behaviour' of computers (Seymour Pappert of MIT) had the idea that a good way to get quite young elementary-school children to find it fun to play about with mathematics was to let them program computers. So he built a mechanical 'turtle', which can move in a straight line, and then turn through some definite angle and go off in a new direction; and it is quite simple to program a computer to tell it when to turn and what angle to turn through; and the computer will go tirelessly on giving the orders out again and again, and the indefatigable turtle will carry them out. And what happens?

The simplest possible instructions are: (1) Go forward one unit length; (2) turn right through a right angle (90°); (3) advance one unit: go back to instruction (1) and repeat until you come to place you have been before, then (4) stop. Of course the turtle just walks out a square (9b.8, left). So to make it a bit more interesting, put in one more step; after order (2) turn right, put in a new order, (3) go two units forward; then go back to instruction (1) and repeat. This just goes round a rectangle, and stops very soon (9b.8, right). We begin to get something

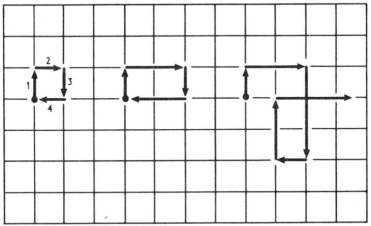

FIG. 9b.8
interesting when we put in a longer sequence of distances the turtle has to go before starting over again with instruction (1); that is, we say: go 1; go 1, then 2; go 1, then 2, then 3; go 1, then 2, then 3, then 4; and so on (turning right angles after each step). The patterns of the turtle's walk,

up to the program where we have put in eight steps of the sequence, are shown in 9b.9. They are, as you see, beginning to get quite amusing. (Note that the programs with four steps, and with eight steps, never stop, but go on for ever.) They are not easy to foresee without actually getting the turtle to do it (or, with a program as simple as this, one can do it with pencil and paper).

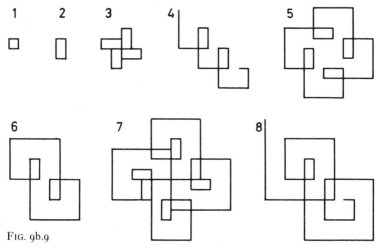

FIG. 9b.9

Then one might try putting in some left turns, instead of right ones. Who would have guessed that if we went on to the next stage in the sequence above, that with nine steps with 90° turns, which are always to the right except that we tell the turtle to turn left after it has taken six steps, it would walk out a pattern like 9b.10?

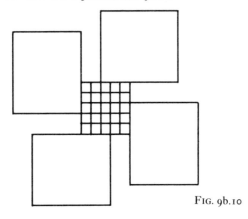

FIG. 9b.10

These patterns are not very simple, but they are still rather boring. Much more interesting things have been produced by a program which is only slightly more complicated. It involves, not right turns, but turns at 60° or 120° – to plot them out with pencil and paper, it is easiest to get hold of one of the special types of graph paper, known as 'isometric paper', which is ruled with three sets of lines at 60° to each other, making a set of equilateral triangles instead of the usual squares. We always start at one point; but now we consider that what we are starting is a 'worm', which can only live by eating its way along a line. (In fact, the whole of this idea started by people trying to understand some very funny patterns of grooves on the surface of ancient muds which have by now turned into rocks; they must be fossil tracks of feeding worms, but how did the worms behave to produce these odd patterns? (See *Science*, 21 November 1969, if you're intrigued.)

When a worm starts off and eats its way along a line, it will soon come to an intersection, where its line meets five other lines. If its program tells it to go straight on, it just does go straight on indefinitely, making a very boring straight line. So it's only interesting if the program tells it to turn; there are two lines on each side into which it could turn, either 'gently' (turning only 60° off track), or 'sharp' (turning 120°); and, of course either left or right. Then, when it does this sort of thing, it may find itself coming up to an intersection at which it has been before, so that some of the lines have already been eaten up, and it has a more restricted range of choices. For example in 9b.11 the solid lines show a worm which eats along the lines according to the instructions; (1) at an intersection with five open lines, turn sharp right; (2) at an intersection with some lines already used (e.g. after step 3), go straight on. This soon leads to a place where all the lines have been eaten out and the worm dies. The dotted lines, starting after step 2, show a worm programmed to: (1) do one sharp right turn, then two sharp left turns, then two sharp right and so on alternately, even at intersections with some lines used up; in the few steps shown, the worm has not yet met a situation which calls for further instructions.

If you work it out (or take the simple way out of looking it up in the *Scientific American*, November 1973), you will find that the number of choices for which the worm may have to be given instructions are really quite few. When a worm sets off, he will first come to an intersection where he is confronted by five lines; if we rule out that he goes straight ahead, because that gives just a boring straight line, there are two choices to be made: turn left or right; turn gently or sharply. Then, at

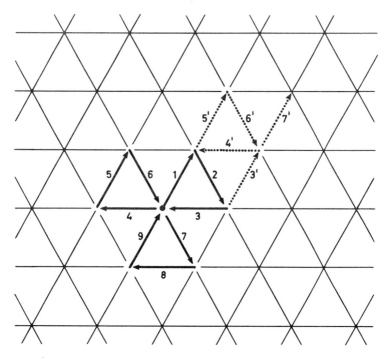

F<small>IG</small>. 9b.11

later stages, the worm may come to points where one, or two, or three, or four, of the lines have been already used up (if all five have, the worm will have to die). It turns out (I won't go into the details), that if one line has gone, there are four possible choices, and the worm has to be instructed which to take; when two lines have gone, one can say that there are four patterns the worm may meet, and for each pattern he has three choices as to how he reacts – a total of twelve instructions has to be given. And if three lines have gone, there are only two to choose between; and with four gone, no choice is left. So with a maximum of 2 + 4 + 12 + 2 = 20 instructions, any worm can be fully clued up what to do in any possible circumstances. Of course, many worms will never come across more than a few of the conceivably possible situations, and can live out a full life with many fewer than twenty instructions, like those described above.

The point to notice here is that even this fairly small number of possible choices (twenty as a maximum) generate an extraordinary num-

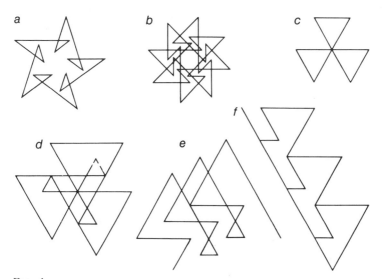

FIG. 9b.12

ber of astonishingly complex and different patterns. Some are open, going on for ever, like 9b.12. Others are 'closed', and eventually come to an end. Some of these closed patterns have a lot of symmetry (9b.13),

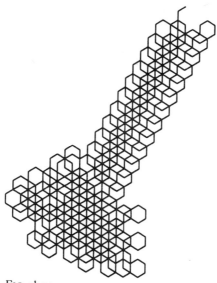

FIG. 9b.13

155

which differs from the open one (9b.12) in only *one* of the twenty instructions. Other closed paths show very little symmetry (9b.13). And the most complex closed path so far worked out – there are quite a lot of programs whose end-results, if any, have not yet been discovered – is a pretty surprising mixture of symmetry and apparent disorder in the middle (9b.14).

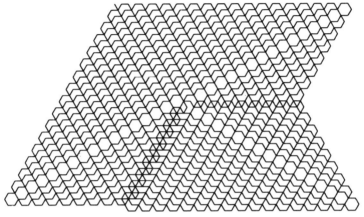

FIG. 9b.14

The point of these games is not merely that they are rather pretty, if you like that sort of thing. Much more important is that they show that the human mind simply is not, at this point in evolutionary time, set up to be of any use in foretelling what will be the final outcome of following some quite simple program of behaviour. Nor can we foresee how the overall appearance of the system will change as its development proceeds. The figure 9b.15 represents a few stages in a program (coded as 5007 by Michael Beeler, who studied it). After 50 moves, it is quite a compact, rather vertical shape; but that soon changes; at step 100 it slopes down to the right; at 200 it is a triangle pointing down; after 500 it has a general horizontal disposition and has some holes in it; by step 1,726, when it has travelled downwards as far as it will ever go, it is looking much more ragged, with several 'teeth' jutting out on the left side; but by step 2,373, when it comes to a sudden and rather unexpected end, most of these teeth have been more or less covered up and smoothed over, though the whole shape has still some holes in it, and looks much less neat and well organized than it did at step 50.

Many of the things we find most important in life are biological or socio-biological systems which operate on the basis of programs of

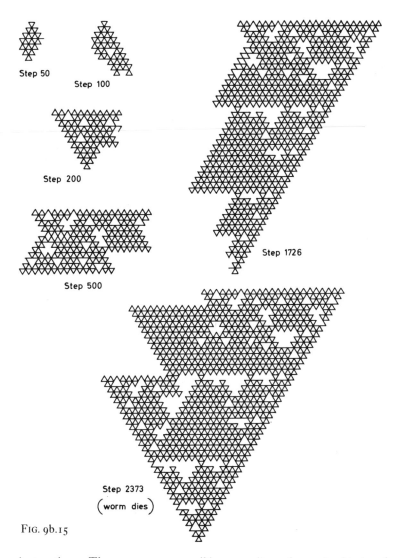

Step 50

Step 100

Step 200

Step 500

Step 1726

Step 2373
(worm dies)

Fig. 9b.15

instructions. These games are striking warnings about the kinds of behaviour we have to expect during the history of societies, or economic systems, or men programmed by their genes; their overall configuration may change in very unexpected ways as further and further steps in the programs become realized, even if there are no changes in the programs themselves. One cannot expect it to be easy to foretell the result of carrying on with one and the same economic system, let alone forecast what will happen if one introduces an alteration of the rules. And what is the sense in discussing genetically limited differences in IQ between races or other human groups, when we have no idea whether their genetic programs are 'terminating' ones, or never reach a final state; and also have no way of knowing how far various people are along the path of working out their program? My guess – it can be no more than a guess – is that no one – Einstein, Plato, Leonardo – has ever yet had the opportunity to develop his mental genetic program to the point where it reaches termination and sets a limit on his capacities. I strongly suspect that most groups of the human race are quite a short way into their development; perhaps for most of history they have been able to get to a fairly comfortable early stage rather like that of program 5007 at step 50, or even 500, and now we may be in something like the more 'messy' stages of growth which that program goes through later.

*Nobody* really understands these systems yet; even though anyone must acknowledge that they are simply very elementary examples of the way much of the world must work. Michael Beeler, who is 'playing' with them, wrote me in a letter:

one interesting aspect is that, if a worm has grown a large, complicated tangle of path segments, there must (easily demonstrated mathematically) always be a trail of uneaten segments leading from wherever it now is back into the original starting point. For large, dense tangles, these trails resemble a channel, like a canal for barges – and it is intriguing to watch the worm wind itself around and around the tangled blob, each time missing the channel until finally it happens to fall into the channel and is then forced to follow it back to the origin and die.

Civilization, working out successive steps in a program of power, energy, competition, builds up a tangled skein of complexities, which always, at step $n$, looks as though you don't need to bother about anything but how to get to step $n + 1$ – and then it hits a situation – the atom bomb? – the Revolt against Reason? – and, as in the game Snakes and Ladders, can't stop till it's back at Square One, the Paleolithic, but this time with all the cream, the easily exploited natural resources, already skimmed off the milk. Perhaps these funny mathematical worms are simply putting into up-stage intellectual terms the point Blake made:

> O ROSE, thou art sick!
> The invisible worm
> That flies in the night,
> In the howling storm,

Has found out thy bed
Of crimson joy,
And his dark secret love
Does thy life destroy.

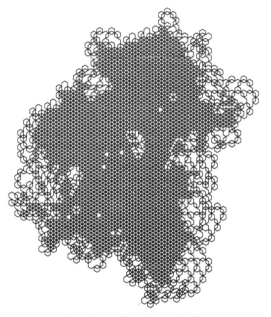

*Cloud path generated by a gentle worm $1_a2_{a!aa}3_c4_a$*

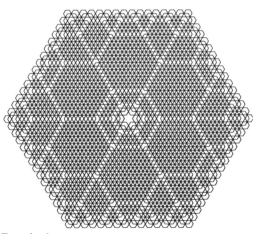

FIG. 9b.16      *The superdoily ($1_a2_{d}3_{c!aa}4_b$)*

Perhaps, as we have seen in other sections of this book, the actual constraints of the fields of action in human society, and the existence of rules more subtle than simple choices (involving feed-backs for instance), tend to limit the effects of our programs to something less outlandish. What we have been illustrating in this section might be called 'runaway' results. It's as well to know what they can be, just to realize that in real life we do not often come across them – actual processes are nearly always homeorhetic, or chreodic.

# 10    Handling Systems

## A. The Theory of Games

In the complex systems that one finds one has to deal with in practice, some of the most important components may be other people. If one is trying to change the system in a particular direction, one has to take into account what steps these other people are also going to take to alter the system. It would be nice if there was a rational theory of how to behave in situations in which one is in conflict or interaction with other actively operating persons. In 1944 the Americans Jon von Neumann and Oskar Morgenstern produced a book called *The Theory of Games and Economic Behaviour* which promised to fill this need. For some time the Theory of Games became a very fashionable subject. More recently, it has gradually been realized that it can do very little in the way of giving practical recipes of how to act within conflicts or games. It certainly does not provide any infallible rules for winning at chess, bridge or poker, let alone games where moves require physical skill, like golf or tennis. At one period it was extensively used by the American military in planning their strategy in the Korean and Vietnam wars – not perhaps very persuasive testimony to its value. However, it does provide some interesting suggestions about how to analyse situations of conflict, sufficiently to get an insight into the type of thinking that is most likely to lead to a useful result. Some of these ideas should be part of everyone's mental equipment.

The Theory is expressed in terms of games rather than of conflicts, the difference being that in a conflict, e.g. a dog-fight, either side may do anything at any moment, whereas in a game (e.g. chess) there are only a certain number of moves that any player may legitimately make. These possible moves may be specified by the rules of the game, as in chess; or they may be a consequence of the practicalities of the situation; for instance, an army commander cannot instantaneously redistribute his forces on the battlefield; he has to choose between the alternatives which his transport arrangements and so on make possible.

To get hold of the most useful ideas which have come up in the attempt to develop a Theory of Games, it is only necessary to consider quite simple games involving only two sides ('two-person games'). The most important ways of classifying two-person games are to ask: is this game of perfect or imperfect information? and is this a zero-sum or non-zero-sum game? In a game of perfect information, each player sees the whole situation and each knows as much about it as does his opponent. These can be very simple games like noughts and crosses (tick-tack-toe in American) or more complicated games like chess. In a game of imperfect information, each player knows his own hand but can only guess at what resources his opponent has, as in most card games, such as bridge or poker. A zero-sum game is one in which the sum of the losses and gains of the two players adds up to zero; that is to say, what A wins B must lose, and vice versa. In a non-zero-sum game this is not so. Both sides may win or both sides may lose, or one side may win much more than the other one loses; in any case the sum of the gains and losses does not cancel out to zero. This is an extremely important distinction to have in mind, since many people seem instinctively to think that all situations of conflict are of the zero-sum type, whereas in reality many of them may not be.

It is perhaps worth illustrating this distinction in a very general context, which is relevant to many of the subjects discussed in this book. In a recent number of *Science* there was an exchange of letters about 'the uses of knowledge', between a leading evolutionary geneticist, R. C. Lewontin, and an engineer, Harvey Brooks, who has for long been very concerned with science policy (*Science 177*, 4 August 1972, p. 386). Lewontin wrote: 'In his article *Can Science Survive in the Modern Age?*, Harvey Brooks describes "an extreme view", which argues that new knowledge can always be more readily used by those with political and economic power, therefore knowledge inevitably leads to concentration of power and is thus inherently evil, at least in the present arrangements of Society.' Lewontin goes on to say that he accepts this proposition as self-evident. However, Brooks replies that he rejects the argument as self-evidently absurd.

Implicit in Lewontin's letter is the assumption that we are dealing with a zero-sum game in which every scientific advance increases the power, freedom, or wealth of one group at the expense of others. My own view is that the principal effect of the Scientific Revolution, especially in the 20th Century, has been to change the nature of the social and economic game from a zero-sum one to a situation where many can benefit without cost to others. We are gradually moving from an economy of scarcity, inevitably based on exploitation of the many by the few, to a society of abundance, in which for the most part the exploitation of one group by another does not pay, even for the exploiter.

*Zero-Sum Games*

Before considering non-zero-sum games in a more formal way, let us first deal with the simpler situation of zero-sum games. The simplest situation is a zero-sum game of perfect information. The procedure here is to draw up a pay-off table (or pay-off 'matrix') for the next move, listing along the top the possible moves open to *a* and down the side the moves open to *b*, and in each square the pay-off to *a* for that particular combination of moves. Since this is a zero-sum game the pay-off to *b* will be the same figures with the signs reversed. Rapoport (*Scientific American*, December 1962, vol. 207, p. 108) gives an example of two companies, Castor and Pollux. They are trying to decide whether to go into an advertisement campaign or not, but Pollux is trying to put Castor out of business and is therefore concerned mainly to make Castor lose money (this makes it a zero-sum game in which Castor's losses are Pollux's gains). Since there are only two possible moves for each side (to advertise or not to advertise), there are only four values in the pay-off table (10a.1).

The main content of the Theory of Games is then to tell you how to play safe in situations of this kind. The strategy it recommends is to ensure that your losses are as small as possible, whatever the other man may do. From Castor's point of view it might lose three if it did not advertise but Pollux does; on the other hand it would lose only one if both advertised; and therefore it will advertise. Again, Pollux, which is trying to make Castor lose money, will certainly settle for advertising. For both sides the sensible, that is to say the least risky, move is clear. It is the move which makes the possible loss as small as it can be. Another way of putting this is that it makes the minimum gain as large as it can be, for that reason it is often known as the 'Minimax' solution; it is the move that maximizes the minimum gain.

*Castor's Pay-Off Table*

|        |               | Castor gains if it advertises | Castor gains if it does not advertise |
|--------|---------------|:-----------------------------:|:-------------------------------------:|
| Pollux | advertise     | $-1$                          | $-3$                                  |
|        | not advertise | $+2$                          | $0$                                   |

*Pollux's Pay-Off Table*

|  |  | if Castor | |
|  |  | advertises | does not advertise |
| Pollux | advertise | +1 | +3 |
| gains | not advertise | −2 | 0 |

The situation is different in a game of imperfect information. One of the players, *a*, can draw up his own pay-off table, showing the way he rates the gains and losses to him that would occur in various combina-

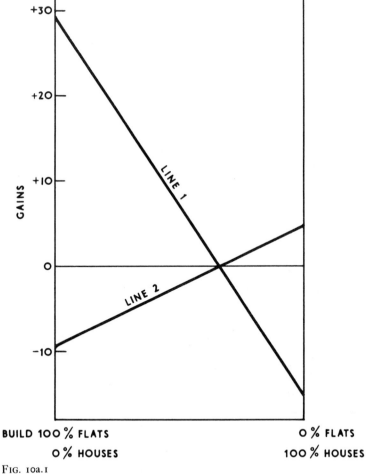

FIG. 10a.1

tions of his next move and of his opponent's move; but he can't know if his opponent rates the value of the moves equally, and he therefore cannot deduce exactly what his opponent is likely to do. In such a case there is no single best move, which is guaranteed to maximize his minimum gain or minimize his maximum loss. The best he can do is to work out the optimum strategy to employ, supposing the same situation occurred again and again or, to put the same thing another way, he can work out the odds that one of his two moves will turn out to be the best he could have done.

The way to do this can be described in terms of imaginary example. Consider a 'game' between a planner, who is to build a new suburb containing some flats and some houses, but has no way of finding out the preferences of the people who are going to live in it; and one of the future citizens, who wants to put his name down for a dwelling giving flats and houses priorities which will partly express his own wishes, and also make sure that he is successful in getting something. The planner can draw up a pay-off table on the basis of what he would 'win' if he built either all flats or all houses, and if the citizens wanted either all flats or all houses (10a.2). Let us suppose that the flats are cheaper to build, or otherwise in some way more desirable from the planner's point of view. If he built all flats and the citizens wanted all flats, he would stand to win, say 30, but if he built all flats and the citizens wanted all houses this might really have to be regarded as a loss of $-10$. On the other hand, if he built all houses and the citizens wanted all flats, he might lose even more, since the houses are more expensive to build; so let's say his loss is $-15$. If he builds all houses and the citizens want all houses, he wins again, but not as much as he did in the situation when both sides go for flats, since houses are more expensive; we rate his win therefore at $+5$.

*Planners' Pay-Off Table*

|  |  | planner gains if he build | |
|---|---|---|---|
|  |  | all flats | all houses |
| citizens want | all flats | $+30$ | $-15$ |
|  | all houses | $-10$ | $+5$ |

Fig. 10a.2

The simplest way he can find out how to play safe is to make a graph, showing the results to *him* of the *possible choices of the citizen*. In 10a.1, if the citizens want flats, the planner either gains 30 if he builds flats, or

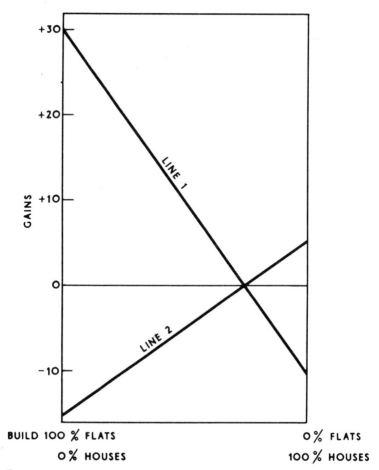


FIG. 10a.3

loses 15 if he builds only houses. If he does a mixture of the two his gain will lie at the corresponding point on line 1 connecting these two points on the graph. Similarly, if the citizen opts for houses the planner's gain will lie somewhere on line 2. If the planner has no way of finding out beforehand which choice the citizen is going to make, his safest bet is to build the mix of flats and houses indicated by the point where these two lines cross; that is to say 2/3 houses and 1/3 flats. If he built more flats he *might*, of course, gain more, but he would win even less if the citizen chooses the wrong way; similarly if he builds more houses.

What happens if we turn round and look at the situation from the citizen's point of view? When he tries to draw up his pay-off table he will take account not only of his own wishes, but also of the knowledge that flats are likely to be somewhat cheaper. Let us suppose in fact that this citizen prefers a flat anyway and, considering its cheapness, prefers it very much. Indeed to make the matter simple, let us assume that he draws up a pay-off table of exactly the same values as the planner's pay-off table (10a.3). But then to discover his optimum strategy, that is to say the safest priorities to give to houses and flats when he puts in his application, he has to draw a *different* diagram (10a.2). He has to consider what would be the gains to *him* according to the various moves the planner might make. Again, to play safe he should express a priority for flats of the degree corresponding to the place where the two lines cross. This turns out to be giving the flats a rating of 3 and houses a rating of 1 (i.e. 75 per cent for flats and 25 per cent for houses).

*Citizen's Pay-Off Table* (10a.3)

|  |  | planner builds | |
|---|---|---|---|
|  |  | all flats | all houses |
| citizen gains if | flats | $+30$ | $-15$ |
| he asks for | houses | $-10$ | $+5$ |

The figures in this example have been chosen so that if both sides play safe neither side gains anything or loses anything. But this is just a chance result of choosing these particular figures. The general principles of drawing up the pay-off matrices, and seeing what will happen when an opponent counters any particular move you make, remains valid even if this condition does not hold, or even if the pay-off tables drawn up by both sides are quite different. However, the whole business of drawing up pay-off matrices of this kind, and then searching for the Minimax, or safest strategy, is all obviously fairly artificial in relation to situations in real life. For instance it leaves out the whole business of bluffing and all the other professional skills of real-games players.

### Non-Zero-Sum Games

We will now turn just to sketch what is meant by a non-zero-sum game. The classical example of such a game, which is quoted in all the books, is a somewhat unlikely situation which is referred to as 'The Prisoner's Dilemma'. The story, which is supposed to take place in some slightly sinister dago part of the world, such as an imaginary Central American republic, is this: Two suspects, Pedro and Carlo, were captured and are being held in separate cells accused of the same crime. They are asked to give evidence against each other; and they are told that if one gives evidence against the other, the evidence will be accepted, the accuser set free and given a reward, and the accused will be executed; but if they both accuse each other, they will both be considered partially guilty, and both condemned to a long sentence. On the other hand, if neither accuses the other, the case will eventually be given up for lack of evidence, and both will eventually go free, though of course not with a reward.

What are the pay-off tables? For Pedro they might look like this:

*Pedro's Pay-Off Table* (Prisoner's Dilemma)

| | | Carlo | |
| --- | --- | --- | --- |
| | | accuses P | does not accuse P |
| Pedro gains if he | accuses C | −20 | +20 |
| | does not accuse C | −100 | +5 |

Now if this was a zero-sum game, whatever Pedro gained Carlo would lose, and vice versa. In that case, Carlo's pay-off table would be exactly the same as Pedro's but with the signs reversed.

*Carlo's Pay-Off Table* (Zero-Sum)

| | | Carlo gains if he | |
| --- | --- | --- | --- |
| | | accuses P | does not accuse P |
| Pedro | accuses C | +20 | −20 |
| | does not accuse C | +100 | −5 |

However, this is *not* zero-sum, but Prisoner's Dilemma, and according to the rules of that game, Carlo's table is different as follows:

*Carlo's Pay-Off Table* (Prisoner's Dilemma)

| | | Carlo gains if he | |
| --- | --- | --- | --- |
| | | accuses P | does not accuse P |
| Pedro | accuses C | −20 | −100 |
| | does not accuse C | +20 | +5 |

These two tables bring out a point, which is fairly obvious, even when the story is first told, namely that if neither Pedro nor Carlo accused each other they would both be fairly well off. However, their difficulty is that neither can be certain, since they have no way of communicating with each other, that the other man would see it this way. It would be fatal for Pedro to refrain from accusing Carlo if Carlo did not choose to play the game the same way, but set about accusing Pedro; and vice versa. So both sides are likely to play the accusation move, and both will suffer reasonably badly.

There are a great many real-life situations in which the essential logic is the same as in this simple story. For instance, disarmament. It would obviously be to the advantage of both sides in an arms race, if they could both disarm; instead each side can only do this if they can be certain that the other party are going to play the game the same way. As Prisoner's Dilemma suggests, the most important factor in enabling them to reach the sensible decision is communication. So long as a game of this kind remains a 'game of imperfect information', the solution which would be best for both parties in the long run can never be reached.

Another pressing situation which falls in the Prisoner's Dilemma category is the 'urban auto'. It would be better all round if everyone (or at least many) used public transport; but in the meantime it is better for each individual to use his own car.

Another important non-zero-sum game is what Garrett Hardin has called 'The Tragedy of the Commons'. Suppose a community possesses a piece of common land, on which anyone is free to graze his cattle – as was usual in medieval England. Any given person will always get more out of the system the more cattle he can put out to graze; and this will remain true even when there are so many that the common is over-grazed and the animals begin to do badly. The move which would then benefit everybody would be for the number of cattle to be reduced to the carrying capacity of the land; but it will never pay any individual to reduce his stock unless everyone else does so too. We are already seeing this problem, on a world scale, in the exploitation of natural resources of many different kinds.

A final type of game-result worth noticing is one which I have called 'hitting the jackpot' (or 'producing a new archetype'), and have discussed particularly in connection with evolution. It happens when, in an attempt to meet some fairly modest short-term goal, the player stumbles on a move which gives him enormously more return than he expected (or perhaps knows what to do with). About the simplest example would be a spongy sort of animal, or group of cells, floating on the surface of some water, protected from the waves by three stiff rods connected by two joints into a longer assembly, flexible at the joints.

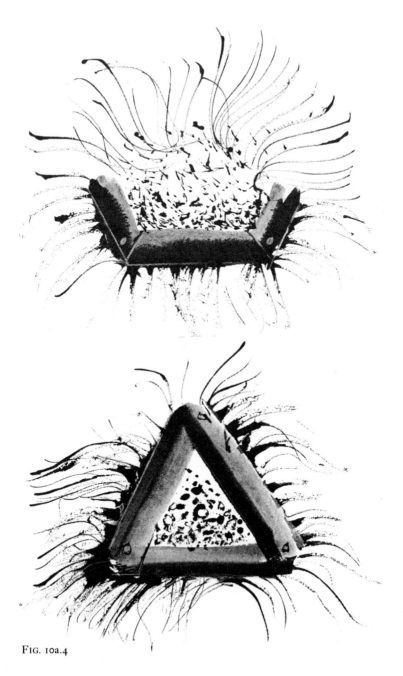

Fig. 10a.4

The protection would be improved if the joints became stiffer, and the whole assembly less flexible; or if the rods became longer. But when the two shortest rods have increased till the sum of their lengths is longer than that of the longest rod, the whole assembly can form a triangle, and its strength goes up enormously. The system has hit a jackpot; or it has found a new archetype (the triangle) from which it can start again to elaborate a new set of developments to meet a new and much tougher set of requirements.

There has been a good deal of jackpot-hitting in recent human history. The discovery of the method of discovery, as Whitehead called it – the Renaissance invention of the controlled experiment as a way of finding out about causal relations in the natural world – unexpectedly tapped the whole jackpot of technology; and we still have little idea how to handle our winnings. Even human language itself may have evolved by the jackpot mechanism. Possibly all that our early ancestors were after was some way for members of a hunting band to communicate more definitely than can be done with inarticulate shouts and grunts; maybe it was useful to be able to say 'It's not in that bush, it's in the clump of reeds; and it isn't a lion, it's a buffalo.' If that was the way it went, they could scarcely have foreseen that the solution they hit on for that practical problem would give them a language, which was bound to produce Homer, Aeschylus, Shakespeare or their equivalents.

## Real Games

Although Games Theory provides some interesting concepts and Tools for Thought, I do not think that by itself it is a very effective tool for actually dealing with complex situations. My own deepest involvement in handling complex practical affairs was in Operational Research (the Aircraft versus the U-Boat game) in World War II, and in breeding dairy cattle in the years immediately thereafter. Games Theory hadn't been invented at that time; but, thinking back, I find it difficult to find any problem where it would have enabled us to do much better than we did without. And I notice that some people who started as fervent advocates, for instance of its application in planning the United States war strategies in Korea and Indo-China, have been led, by the, let us say, not glamorously successful results, to sound warnings about its limitations (e.g. A. Rapoport, *Strategy and Conscience*).

There are several reasons, which can be expressed in general terms, for foreseeing difficulties in getting in practice all the benefits which seem possible in theory. In the first place, in any really complicated game, it may still be possible to see how to work out a complete pay-off table in theory, and how to select the best move out of it; but the computations involved may just be too voluminous to be practical, even with the best of modern computers. For instance, in chess there are firm rules governing the type of move that can be made by the various pieces, and in theory one could work out the best move to make, from any initial set-up, by working out all the possible variants of the next ten, or twenty, or thirty moves; but in practice the number of possible variants soon becomes so fantastically large that one can only work them out for quite a few moves ahead, too few to be really useful in guiding the game. That is why chess-playing computers have so far just got into the good amateur class, but not beyond it. They require some new strategy for searching the vast array of future possibilities to find the optimum (or at least, a near-optimum, 'satisfying') move.

Again, in real-life situations to which one might want to apply Games Theory to get practically useful answers, one will usually be trying to improve some already ongoing procedure. *Any* change in such a procedure usually carries quite a price-tag; it may mean re-equipping, or re-training operatives, or altering administrative organization, and so on. In my wartime RAF experience, when there was enormous pressure to get results, and to get them fast (war doesn't wait), it was practically never worth making any change unless it looked like bringing in an improvement of 50 per cent or more – chiefly because most changes required either re-training, or complication of maintenance organization, and such things, which both took time and diverted production effort. The limitation would not be so stringent in peacetime operations, where you can afford to think in years rather than in months, and where really minute differences in efficiency, of fractions of a per cent return on expenditure, may have time to mount up to real importance. But the general principle remains; a practical pay-off table should show, not merely what moves are possible, and what the returns on them will be considering what the other chap may do; but, also, how much will it cost you to make each of the theoretically possible moves.

In most real-life games, adding to your information about the situation is probably even more important than carefully thinking out a detailed pay-off table. From this point of view one could classify games into two types: those in which you are playing against an impersonal opponent (a farmer planning the planting of his crops, not knowing what the weather is going to do) or against such numerous opponents that they have to be treated as an impersonal statistical force (e.g. playing the stock market); or, on the other hand, games in which you are playing against a single intelligent opponent (as the general staff of the USA and USSR are playing against each other in the nuclear arms race).

In the first type, it would obviously be very important to the farmer if there were reliable long-range weather forecasts; and the stockbroker has to pick up any hints he can as to how the market is likely to move. In the person-to-person games, trying to find out what the other chap is up to may be worth almost as much effort as making the actual moves of the game itself. For instance, in the RAF Coastal Command game against the German U-boats it was absolutely essential to discover such things as whether a U-boat could listen to the radar which we were using to find them, and whether, when they discovered a convoy and attacked it, each U-boat was acting more or less independently, or used some organization; say one U-boat shadowing the convoy close in, signalling the rest of the pack of U-boats to get into appropriate positions to intercept it later on in its course. The answers to such questions do not come out of Games Theory, but rather they demand operational research of the kind discussed on pp. 189–197. In the nuclear armament race, discovering what the other side is up to is absolutely the kernel of the problem, showing one what problems one may have to tackle, and also, in more favourable circumstances, giving reasons to believe that a threat that might be anticipated is not actually likely to arise. In all these situations, investigations by methods such as operational research, or by spying, or photographic reconnaissance or any other suitable technique, has a lot more to offer in practice than the abstract Theory of Games has.

## B. Time Budgeting

There is one group of methods, developed mainly in connection with industrial operations and usually involving some rather mild degree of technological forecasting, which it is quite useful to become acquainted with. Suppose you want to carry out some project which essentially involves bringing to fruition quite a large number of sub-projects. How do you organize the sequence in which to tackle the various steps in the overall procedure? Really complicated situations of this kind arise, for instance, in organizing a moonshot – or in a far less complicated but still formidable scale, in the opening of a theatrical performance. Everything has got to be ready on the night, and some of those things may have taken months, or even years, to get ready, others only weeks or days. It would be silly to start off by fixing something which only takes a few days, when some other essential part of the whole scenario is going to take two years (by which time the few-day item will probably have gone out of date).

The principle to follow has, as usual, been given a suitably impressive jargonized name – 'Critical Path Analysis' – and, as usual, is basically extremely simple in conception. Suppose that there are, in a relatively simple case, twelve different things that have to be done. Write them all down and number them from one to twelve. It will be obvious that some of the projects cannot be started until some others have been completed. If you are going to put on a play, it is no use worrying about the lighting before you have decided in which theatre it's going to be, and have worked out at least the general notion of what sort of scenery is to be provided. The principle of critical path analysis is to decide what is the unavoidably *longest* sequence of steps which will have to be taken; and then to use this as a framework into which you can fit all the other essential, but not so time-demanding, sub-projects.

It will be easier to see what this means in terms of a concrete example. Djerassi – a professor at the University of California and also the President of Syntex Corporation, a 'high technology' outfit that made the initial breakthrough which produced cheap and massive supplies of the sex hormones required for the present-day contraceptive pill – has considered what would be involved in the production of any radically new contraceptive agent. He is talking about something which is not just a minor variation on what we have already, but which works on some different principle, giving an effect of a more acceptable kind; for instance, a morning-after pill, or an agent which could be added to a staple food such as bread or salt, sterilizing everybody until they took an antidote to it. Djerassi points out that there are not only a lot of scientific technical problems to be solved before any such totally new contraceptive could be produced, but legislation in the United States (and in most other advanced countries) stipulates that a whole series of tests have to be carried out, on the toxicity (poisonousness), teratological effects (damage to the foetuses of pregnant women) and other such biological side-effects, before the drug could be put on the market. It would be necessary to work out the best way of compounding the new

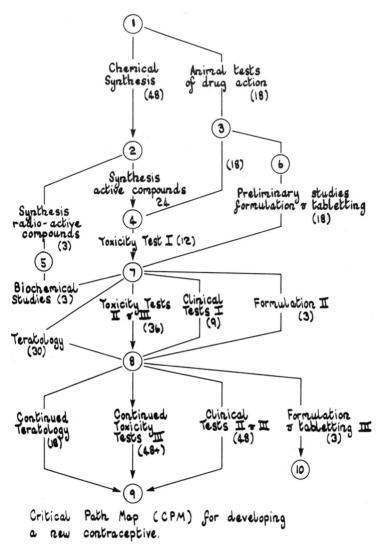

Critical Path Map (CPM) for developing a new contraceptive.

FIG. 10b.1

drug with other substances, and how to incorporate it into a suitable tablet – should it be one which is absorbed rapidly, or gradually over a much longer period?

Djerassi's critical path analysis for this project is shown in 10b.1. Of all the various things which have to be done, there is one sequence of steps, of which the later ones could not be begun until the earlier ones were finished, which dictates the minimum overall time the project is bound to take. Other things that have to be done would take shorter times, and could be fitted in while the most time-demanding steps were being gone through.

Estimating the time required for various steps involves a certain amount of forecasting, but there are some steps which could not be shortened. For instance, there are legal obligations to test the substance, administered to a group of animals such as mice, not only on their children, but on their grandchildren; it takes just so much time to produce those grandchildren. On the other hand, some steps may take longer in practice than they need to do in theory, if something goes wrong during the course of experiments. However, in spite of the uncertainties of forecasting, in practical situations it is often possible to get a very good idea of which particular sequence of steps is going to be limiting in time, and should therefore be pressed on with as fast as possible. This sequence is the 'Critical Path'.

A look at the time budget which Djerassi provides (and at the cost estimates he makes for the various steps) shows that developing any really radically new contraceptive agent is a major undertaking. The claim has been made that under the Public Health constraints and testing procedures laid down in the United States (and in most of the rich westernized countries) many of our standard medicaments (e.g. aspirin) would never have emerged as commercial projects if these regulations for protecting the public had been enforced at the time they were invented. It is clear that no one with a bright idea for a new useful drug can hope to get it off the ground unless he can find financial backing to go on testing for conceivable harmful effects for quite a number of years. This protects the public, but also puts the whole power of initiative into the hands of the major rich pharmaceutical firms. Possibly the future of the development of really novel types of medical agents – contraceptive or other – will shift into countries such as Brazil, or India, whose biological problems are so pressing that they will be more interested in finding something which will do an immediate important job than to have 1,000 percentage assurance that it will never have *any* possible harmful effects at long term – just as they prefer to get rid of malaria by using DDT, even if the most aggressive predators in the local fauna, such as eagles and vultures, suffer a bit in consequence.

There is another form of time-budgeting, in which some external agency lays down the minimum time which has to be spent and the problem is how best to fit side-issues in. This is the problem facing university students. They cannot get their degree (ordinary) under three years, or (Honours) under four. Their problem is therefore, how do they allocate time to various interests within a three- or four-year period.

The problems that arise are:

(a) Within this minimum period laid down by the regulations, what hurdles are there that will have to be surmounted, e.g. various critical exams at particular times.

(b) At what level do you aim to get over these hurdles? Getting Firsts or Distinctions all the way through? Or pulling up sharply with a sprint at the end, and getting a First only in the finals. Or just getting through.

(c) In the light of this, how much time will you probably have to spend to achieve the level you are aiming at? Maybe you already know enough chemistry to get a good pass in years one and two, or can be pretty confident of writing an acceptable essay on Wordsworth or Shelley. But maybe you want to take some course where you will have to start right at the beginning and devote a lot of time to your lectures, reading or lab work. If so, in which year will the real pressure come? Budgeting your time like this, you may reckon that in the second year, for instance, you might really have some time to study something interesting even if it doesn't contribute directly to your degree. Life being what it is, it probably won't work out like that – it may turn out that your second year, when you thought you might be free for intellectual development, will actually involve a love affair which will not only mop up all your supposed free time, but carve into the hours you had put aside for surmounting the essential hurdles. But even if the best time-budgeting for the future doesn't always work out 100 per cent, the exercise of trying to do it is likely to force you to realize what is actually going on in your life, of which you could otherwise remain completely unaware.

## C. Meeting Conflicting Requirements

In the world as it is, we are nearly always operating in situations in which we would like to achieve several quite different goals. We are playing games with our eyes not on only one, but on quite a number of pay-off tables. The conventional way of handling this has been to break our total aspirations down into a collection of sub-goals, and to concentrate on each one of these independently. We want transport; so we go for better and faster transport. We want lots of manufactured articles; so we invent labour-saving ways of getting them cheap. We want living accommodation; so we build as many flats or houses as we can, for as little capital outlay as possible, wherever we can find land to put them. Whenever we can recognize A NEED, we try to satisfy THAT NEED, without reference to anything else.

The jargon name for this strategy is 'sub-optimization' – which does not mean (as it might do) looking for something below the optimum, but is used to denote a policy of optimizing each sub-goal separately.

It works reasonably well when the whole society or economic system is growing fast overall. If we push the sub-goal of transport to its practical limit, and this has some unfortunate consequences elsewhere, such as splitting up farming units, or residential districts, by more or less uncrossable roads or railways – well, that does not matter much if the farms or suburbs are themselves making a lot of progress in some other direction on their own. The snags come when the overall situation gets tight. Then sub-optimization tends to put us into the classical situation of 'robbing Peter to pay Paul'. And that is, in many people's opinion, the sort of situation we face in most of mankind's affairs today. Speed up car transport in towns – but we cannot any longer assume that the amenities of decent housing can absorb the impact; save even more labour in manufacture and trade – and maybe there are not any other worthwhile jobs for taking up the redundant man-power. We have to think how to play our hand best in the light of pay-off tables which genuinely do conflict.

*Theory*

Of course one cannot give, in a few paragraphs, hard and fast rules which will show the best way of making such decisions in all circumstances. What I shall attempt here is to suggest one of the more recent ways of thinking about such problems of strategy. The ideas involved are quite difficult; and this is one of the sections in this book which no one need feel ashamed of skipping.

To simplify the situation, suppose there are two possible strategies of action, A and B, and two demands, P and Q; and suppose A is very effective in dealing with demand P, and B in dealing with demand Q. The problem is to decide the right mix of A and B to cope with a situation which presents these two demands in some combination or other. (E.g. suppose mankind consisted of only two major types,

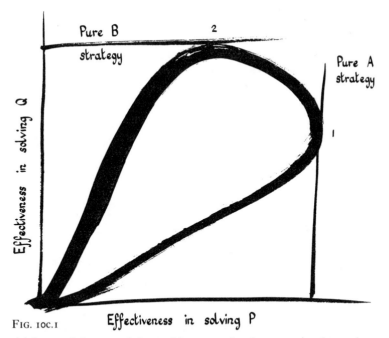

Pure B strategy

2

Pure A strategy

1

Effectiveness in solving Q

FIG. 10C.1    Effectiveness in solving P

thinkers and doers, and the world presented only two major demands, to understand some question, and to do something about it.)

We first make a drawing representing effectiveness of actions. Plot effectiveness-in-solving-P horizontally, and effectiveness-in-solving-Q vertically, and draw a curve showing the best that can be done by any possible combination of A and B (10c.1 and 10c.2). If it is a combination with negligible effectiveness in dealing with P it is likely to be not much better at coping with Q, so the curve will come down to the origin point; people who can hardly think cannot do much either. But a strategy which is all A will be maximally effective in dealing with P and a bit effective, though perhaps not much, in coping with Q; and the opposite strategy, all B, will be vice versa. So the curve will be something like those drawn.

There is an important difference between these two curves. It is related to the degree of antagonism between the two types of specialization. The drawing on the left (10c.1) shows a situation in which the pure strategy A, adapted to solving problem P, also does not do too badly in coping with Q; and the best available way of dealing with Q is not too helpless when faced with P. The two best available strategies are not too drastically specialized. In the drawing that follows (10c.2) they are; to

179

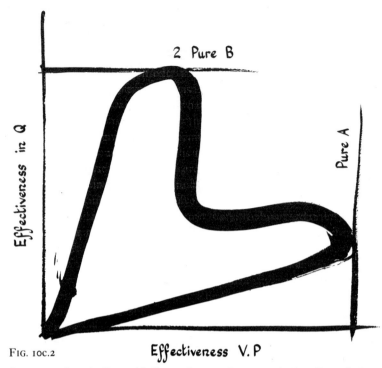

FIG. 10C.2     **Effectiveness V. P**

do very well at dealing with P, you have to be pretty bad at Q, and vice versa. The result is that, in the drawing on the left (generalists with a bit of specialization), the part of the curve between 1 and 2 is convex; while on the right (specialists with only a little general capacity) it is concave.

The difference is that, on the left, the best thinkers are not too bad as doers, the best doers can think a bit for themselves, and one can find people who are quite good at both tasks. On the right, good thinkers break everything they lay their hands on, and practical men are practically morons, while people who try to do a bit of both (on the concave part of the curve) are not much good at either.

Now we have to marry up these curves of possible action-effectiveness with some other curves expressing the demands made by the actual situation. So we will make some other graphs, showing demands for P and demands for Q. If the situation calls only for P, this will give a line which is parallel to the P axis; if for Q, it will be parallel to the Q axis (10c.3 and 10c.4). If there is a mixture of P and Q, which is the interesting situation, one has to ask; what sort of a mixture? It may be 'fine-grained'; demand for P changes to demand for Q, and back again,

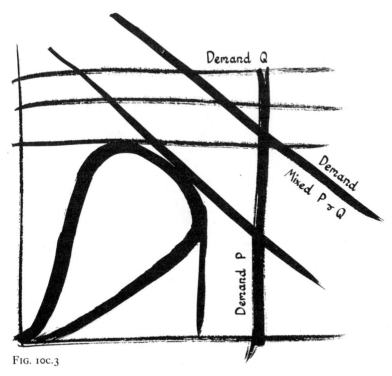

Demand Q

Demand
Mixed P & Q

Demand P

Fig. 10c.3

quite quickly. There will be an intellectual problem to be solved by a thinker in June, but then we will want a doer for July and August. Or it can be 'coarse-grained'; there will be enough intellectual problems to occupy the whole lifetime of a thinker, and also enough practical problems to keep some other people, doers, doing their stuff the whole of their lifetimes.

If the demands are a fine-grained mixture of P and Q, we can express them by a straight line whose slope depends on the proportion of the two demands (10c.3 and 10c.4). The best strategy when the effectiveness curve is convex will then be some intermediate between pure A and pure B; for example to produce people who are quite good thinkers and quite good doers – moderate generalists in fact; or to take decisions which are compromises between the two demands. However, if the effectiveness curve is concave, the generalists or compromises are just too ineffective, and the best that can be done is to settle for either pure A or pure B, depending on which demand is most frequent.

If the demands are coarse-grained, this may be represented by curved

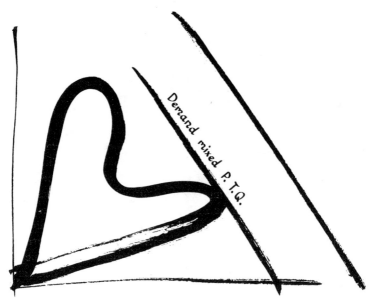

FIG. 10c.4

lines instead of straight ones (10c.5) (I will not go into the explanation of this, which is rather complicated). Again, with a convex effectiveness curve, the best strategy will be a generalist or set of compromises. But with a concave curve, the best strategy may now be a mixture of A and B. The overall effectiveness of mixtures of A and B will be represented by the line joining the points 1 and 2, and the best proportion in which to use them will be given by the place where the demand curve touches this line.

*Democratic Practice*

Finally, a word should be said about the most complex task of 'meeting conflicting requirements' – it is complex, but it is exceedingly common in real life. It is the problem of how to make it more probable that something satisfactory will be done when, at the beginning, one does not know what the conflicting requirements are. This is the situation which faces everyone who is trying to improve or alter a condition in which many other people are involved; how is one to know what they really want? The old conventional answer was that someone – the decision-maker – told them what would be good for them. We are too committed

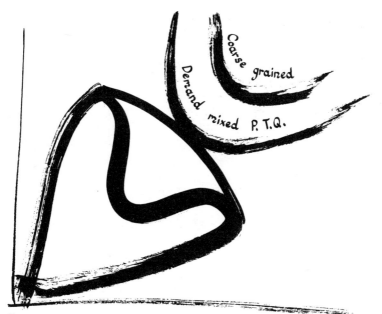

Fig. 10c.5

to democratic ideas to find that satisfactory. The next step is for the decision-maker – say, the planner of a new town – to draw up a blueprint, or even a few alternative blueprints – and give the people who will be displaced by the slum clearance, or who will live in the new town, an opportunity to vote on them. But votes cannot take place often enough. Too much gets done – has to be done – between one vote and the next; and anyway all the 'people' get is an opportunity to choose one or another fixed menu, when what they would like would be to pick and choose *à la carte*.

New ways of organizing decision-making, so as to allow the emergence into effectiveness of the multiple and usually initially conflicting requirements of many affected individual persons, are being explored both in theory and practice. There is space to mention only one of these attempts to systematize 'participatory decision-making'. One of the most fully worked out is described in the book *The RSVP Cycles: Creative Processes in the Human Environment* by the Californian architect-planner Lawrence Halprin – he is married to a modern dance-choreographer who uses much the same methods to put on her performance as he does to develop an area of the country.

His basic notion is that of the 'score'. The British eye, coming on this

183

word in the context of Games Theory, is likely to think of the tally of runs at cricket, or goals at soccer. What Halprin is alluding to is more like a musical score. A printed score of a piece of Bach or Mozart is not a blueprint which has to be followed exactly, so that what the various performers do – Rubinstein, Rostropovich or Richter – is just a question of how competent each of them is in placing every brick in its precisely defined position. The score is an indication, a suggested line of action, which will have no body, no actuality, until the actors or performers work out and actually do the actions into which they think it should be interpreted. In modern music or dance, the scores leave much more freedom to the interpreter–performer than the old ones, which allowed him to decide: a piano or harpsichord? and a bit to do with tempo and stress, and that was about all.

In Larry Halprin's scheme, therefore, if you find yourself playing a 'game' of this sort, you should not make a definite move; you should draft a score, tailored to fit any external constraints, but requiring a lot of input from the people affected (the performers) to turn it into a blueprint specific enough to enable anyone actually to start assembling bricks and mortar.

It is the interaction of the performer with the score that he calls the RSVP cycle. RSVP – as Halprin says 'a communications idea meaning "respond" '; to the European, a well-known French contraction, common at the end of letters or formal invitations, for 'répondez, s'il vous plaît'. In his interpretation they stand for:

R   resources which are what you have to work with (the opposite of the constraints mentioned above);
S   scores, which describe the process leading to the performance;
V   valuation, which analyses the results of the action. The term is coined to suggest the action-oriented as well as the decision-oriented aspects of V in the cycle;
P   performance, which is the resultant of scores and is the 'style' of the process.

Halprin argues that these phases constitute a cycle, which can be entered at any point. The planner/decision-maker, who used to be so authoritarian, enters at S, with a score; but after the performers have put a valuation on it leading to a performance, the circle comes round again. It turns out that there are resources, for instance of personal effort, which the planner did not know of at the start, but which the performance has brought to light; and the score has to be rewritten. And so on, several times round, as the whole enterprise gradually comes to fruition organically, with the participation of everyone involved in it.

For instance, in a project to improve some run-down part of a city, one would try to get together a number of the people living there, or who might later live there. They would need the help of a 'process leader', who would suggest some initial scores – which might be walks along certain routes, on which everyone would see the same cross-section of the place, but probably draw different conclusions from it; or it might be to estimate how easy the household shopping would be from various places if you were getting a bit old and shaky on your pins and hadn't a car. Then there would have to be a 'recorder', who just put down, without editing or expurgating it, the gist of what the members of the group had to say about their experiences in following out the scores. And from these records the process leader would have to lead into another set of processes, with another bunch of scores, and so on, till as much agreement had been reached as seemed possible, given the inherent tendency of individuals to resist being sucked into any sort of consensus.

The system, as described in a couple of pages, sounds a bit Utopian. But it is one example, out of many, of the ways in which Games Theory, or 'Decision Theory' – those jargonized pachyderms of the intellectual ecosystem of our times – might be tamed for human use in a democratic society.

## D. Dealing With an Unpredictable Future

In practice, what we want to do with a complex system often involves not merely the difficult enough task of reconciling different types of requirement, which we have just discussed; we confront what at first sight seems an even more daunting challenge, namely to plan how to adapt the system to the future, even when we realize that we cannot possibly tell what the future will be. Many people seem to think that this is obviously impossible. In fact, one of the conventional responses to any talk of planning for the future is to say that the only thing certain about the future is that it will not turn out as it was expected to be – from which the conclusion is drawn that planning to deal with it is a waste of time, and that we should stop even trying to think about it. But in fact, finding some way of coping with an unpredictable future has been the main challenge which living things have been faced by, and have done a reasonably good job of meeting, throughout their whole evolutionary history, from the earliest organisms which emerged from the primordial soup, right up to the present day.

The organisms which have been evolutionarily successful, that is to say which have left offspring to form later generations, are just those which have found some way of surmounting unforeseen changes in the circumstances of their life; perhaps a new Ice Age, or a new virus disease, or a new predator like a lion or tiger. Many, of course, have failed on the way. Comparatively few thousand years ago there was a very rich fauna of large animals on the American continent, then that most dangerous of all predators – man – got into the continent towards the end of the Ice Age, over the frozen Bering Straits; and as he gradually advanced southwards through North America into South America, he seems to have indulged in the policy of 'over-kill', eliminating many species entirely and decimating some others, until they were very few and far between. Only certain of the previously existing species, such as the buffalo and a few others, found themselves equipped with means of dealing with this new and unforeseeable attack.

A capacity to be able to deal with changed circumstances requires that the agent shall be able to alter his own course of behaviour. Moreover, if the type of change in circumstance that will occur cannot be foreseen, then the acting agent needs to have at his disposal a considerable range of behaviours, and will be able to get away with it if one at least of these is reasonably appropriate. Being able to do several different things almost inevitably involves some sacrifice of the very highest levels of performance at the normal task. Biological systems during their evolution have produced some very ingenious ways of retaining flexibility to meet unforeseen demands without sacrificing too much in immediate efficiency when dealing with the normal prevailing circumstances. They have done considerably better than evolving into 'a Jack of all trades, who is a master of none'. What we have learned about the biological world suggests that the most successful strategy is to become, not so much an all-rounder who can at a moment's notice do any of a large number of things quite reasonably well, but rather to develop into a being who normally does one thing and does it extremely well, but has hidden away and not normally in use a number of other potentialities for doing quite different things, which can at a pinch be called upon and, perhaps after some interval of preparation, be put into operation.

Biological organisms have to meet unforeseen futures on two different time-scales. Firstly, within the course of a normal lifetime, situations may change rather radically and be dealt with by appropriate modifications. Extreme examples are, for instance, some plants which may grow in a pond so that part of the stems and leaves are under water, while another part lifts up above the water's surface and grows in air; or again, as with many insects, one part of the life cycle may be spent, say, as a caterpillar, eating the leaves of plants, and another part of the same individual's life as a butterfly, flitting about from flower to flower. In both these cases we find that one and the same organism may switch completely from one appearance and type of behaviour to another when the circumstances change. In the plant, the leaves growing under water may have quite a different shape from those growing in the air; and, of course, the caterpillar is a very different-looking creature from the butterfly.

Of course, in neither of these cases is it really true to say that the changed circumstances are unpredictable. It is probably fair to say that the caterpillar itself does not foresee the change; but a similar change has happened to very many of its ancestors, and the capacity to switch from caterpillar to butterfly has been gradually evolved over a very long course of generations. Very few animals have the capacity to make such radical changes in response to altered circumstances, unless those alterations have happened to their ancestors and evolution has been able to gradually produce the necessary apparatus. Some of the higher animals can react fairly fast to some changes, such as, for instance, the seagulls which adopt a new method of feeding when people start ploughing fields near the sea-coast. On the whole, however, it is only man who has developed the capacity to respond rapidly to very drastic changes during his individual lifetime. Many people, particularly in recent generations, have acquired a habit of, if not a taste for, radical discontinuous changes of life-style, say from an advertising executive to a drop-out in a commune, and then on to a university student reading for a degree, or to a lorry driver. When such a person is in one of his life-styles, the other potential life-styles are usually rather deeply buried within him and do little to interfere with what he is doing at the moment (see p. 27). This is a very different type of strategy from that of just being a good all-rounder.

The non-human living world is better in dealing with the unforeseeable future in terms of evolution rather than individual development. The thing that evolves is, of course, a population of animals existing through a number of generations. As time goes on, something is almost certain to happen which has never occurred in the past, such as a new disease or predator, or the appearance of a new possible foodstuff. All the higher organisms – that is to say, every living thing except bacteria and viruses – have adopted a very remarkable strategy for dealing with this situation. They normally carry two of each type of hereditary factor, one obtained from their father and one from their mother. These two are very frequently slightly different. Since any given organism has something like 100,000 different hereditary factors (and, we have seen, two representatives of each), the whole population of millions of organisms contains an enormous and varied assemblage of them, which is known as its 'gene pool'. Every individual in the population can be regarded as a sample – a handful as it were – of genes taken out of this gene pool. Now, the remarkable thing is that by no means all the different genes in an organism come to expression under normal circumstances. The development of organisms tends to be canalized in the way discussed in Chapter 7. Developmental processes leading to the formation of, say, a liver or a hand, go along a canalized channel, and a normal liver, carrying out the proper functions in digestion, or a normal hand with five fingers, nearly always appears whatever sample of genes that individual happens to have got out of the gene pool.

Many of the minor variants between the genes are in fact buffered out of expression, and if one just looks at the normal animals in the normal circumstances one would not realize that they were there at all. However, they are still present in the population, and this is what gives the population as a whole such an ability to adapt itself to an extraordinarily wide range of circumstances that may turn up. If a new disease appears, or if somebody starts spraying a population of flies or mosquitoes with DDT, it is very likely that somewhere within the enormous range of genes in the population's gene pool there would be some unexpressed hereditary factor which could confer greater disease resistance or ability to withstand the DDT poison. Such genes may be quite rare, but in a very few individuals they will come to expression, and if DDT is present in the environment those individuals which show the effect of this hereditary factor and are resistant to DDT will survive better and leave more offspring than those who cannot, so the frequency of that factor will increase. After quite a short interval as evolution goes – ten, twenty or thirty generations or so – the great majority of the population would be composed of individuals which are resistant; as we have found to our cost when trying to get rid of the malaria mosquito and various other insect pests of man and his crops. This is a mechanism which confers very great powers of adaptation to unforeseen circumstances, at very little cost in lowering efficiency at normal tasks, since the flexibility is due to the presence of genes whose effects are normally suppressed by the buffering of development.

It is not easy to see how man can make increased use for his own progress in the immediate future of the evolutionary mechanism we have just described. It is important, however, that he should not do anything to weaken this biological mechanism with which evolution has endowed him, as it has endowed all other species. Man's flexibility to meet unforeseen circumstances that will certainly arise in the long-term future depends on the presence within his population of many hereditary potentialities which are not used at present, but which could be used if they were called for. It is most important that man should not try to obtain uniformity of hereditary potentials at the cost of eliminating these unused potentialities, which, when they do come through to expression at the present time, result in people who may seem a bit eccentric or unconventional.

However, even if man cannot do much in the short term to improve this evolutionary potentiality adaptation in his own species, it seems likely that he might use it as a valuable guide in designing some of the self-controlling and adaptable machines whose possibilities he will be exploring in the world of automation and computerization. The strategy of aiming for a system which switches between different alternatives, rather than one that does a bit of everything all at once, is a lesson which nature teaches; and it seems worth learning.


# E. Operational Research

It is not enough to understand complex systems. Often one has to operate on them in some way. Are there any general principles which can help one decide how? This topic is often referred to nowadays as 'Decision Theory'. But like several other newly invented, alleged branches of science, with grandiose titles, this theory suffers from an over-elaboration of language and an inappropriate simplicity of ideas.

In practice, the best procedures for taking executive decisions which will lead to action depend crucially on the speed with which things are happening, and the length of time for which one expects to be involved. If things are happening very fast – the person on the other side of the tennis net has just shot over his best cannonball service – there is nothing to do but to play by ear, or eye, and hope for the best; practically the only conscious decision to be taken is whether to go all out for a quick win or whether to play safe and keep in the game and aim at wearing the other fellow out.

If things are happening rather more slowly, and if one expects to have to go on dealing with the situation for a fairly extended period of time, there is much more opportunity to improve on one's first off-the-cuff decision as to how to deal with it. The most important step is enshrined in the classical answer given to the little boy who asked his father if the oranges were sweet: 'Suck it and see.' Note that this advice contains two parts: act on the system in some way – suck it; and then 'see' what the result is, and modify your actions accordingly. Polysyllabizing – apply some defined input to the system, and monitor the results so as to obtain informational feed-back of its reactions.

This sounds simple advice; but there are two crucial points to note about it. In the first place it is astonishing how often in conventional practice the second step of ascertaining the actual results produced by the first set of actions is neglected. For instance, Great Britain started building new towns on a fairly large scale shortly after the end of World War II; but no arrangements were made to discover what actually happened in the new towns after they were built. Since its inception the new-town policy has undergone several considerable changes, so that people speak of three or four generations of towns, designed in rather different ways. These changes were not the results of carefully collected facts about the social structures which actually grew up in new towns or the responses of people to them, but were based only on much vaguer hunches and casually formed opinions. A second point is that this advice essentially denies the argument that is very often advanced, namely one cannot do anything in this situation until there has been more research. Or rather, the 'suck it and see' point of view implies that what is needed is real experimental research, in which the situation is changed and the result of the change ascertained, rather than 'research' in the non-experimental sense of collecting more information, ascertaining more opinions, and comparing the analysed situation with which you are trying to deal with other unanalysed situations which other people have dealt with elsewhere, and at other times.

Probably the most consistent, thorough-going and comprehensive attempt to apply the 'suck it and see' principle to actual decision-making was developed in the form of Operational Research Sections, particularly those attached to the Royal Air Force during World War II. These were groups of scientists, drawn from many disciplines, who attempted to assist the Commander in Chief of the Force to improve his decisions by scientific study of the results of operations which had been carried out in accordance with his previous executive orders. The type of science involved is neither pure science nor applied science, as these terms are conventionally employed. From the standpoint of the executive, pure science is well away in the background. A certain part of the Air Force may be fighting its battle by dropping depth charges on to submarines; but its Commander in Chief will not be at all immediately concerned with the pure science of underwater explosions and the peculiar behaviour of the gas bubble near the surface. Applied science will take that fundamental theory, and use it to design and produce a depth charge; and again the Commander in Chief will hardly want to go into great detail in his knowledge of it. The immediate problem, as he sees it, is whether he is sinking as many submarines as he might. What has been called the operational research level of science is to take this problem in its entirety, just as it arises at the Commander's staff meeting, and to apply scientific analysis to it.

The aim of this analysis must be to find out what is, in practice, the limiting factor on efficiency, and if there are any 'soft spots' (see p. 91). Of course, bigger bombs would make bigger explosions; but in general an aircraft that carries bigger bombs must carry fewer of them, and will the increase in size of explosion be worth the reduction in number? Or is the crux of the matter somewhere quite different? Perhaps no increase in size or number of bombs will bring any improvement unless the accuracy of aiming can be increased. Or it may be that bombs are being dropped too close together, or set to explode at too great a depth to injure submarines sufficiently near the surface to provide a good aiming mark. The operational research worker must attempt to assess all these possible factors. And as a result of his analysis he should be able to advise the Commander whether he should apply to an applied optics scientist for an improved sight, or to the explosives laboratories for better bombs, or to the psychologists for better methods of training or selecting air crew, or to instrument makers for better altimeters to enable aircraft to fly lower without danger, or to any of the other applied science establishments which he has to fall back on.

Operational research analysis is likely to be the more valuable, the more the problem under investigation is a new one and in a fresh and comparatively little-understood field. In a problem which has been considerably worked on, many of the factors are likely to have emerged and even been quantitatively estimated, without a systematic operational research approach. To take an example, the authorities will have found out for themselves what proportion of traffic accidents are due to defective equipment, what proportion are between vehicles of different speed characteristics, whether segregating slow and fast traffic streams increases or decreases danger, and so on. Even in such a field, war experience suggests that systematic operational research would give results. But it is more called for in newer fields of endeavour, such as the development of backward or colonial countries. If one sets out to raise the standard of life of a region, is the crucial limitation one of deficiency in diet, or of endemic disease? If it is a matter of food, should this be locally produced, or imported against some commodity which the region could export? Must the inhabitants first be taught to read and write before they can better themselves appreciably; and if so, is the crux the provision of school teachers, or perhaps the supply of barbed wire to fence in the cattle and relieve the children of the work of herding? Would the fields be more productive if the people grew other crops, or is the first requisite more water, or more fertilizer, or a system of crop rotation, or a change in the legal basis of land tenure? Are there sources of power available, and could they be used; or must transport first be provided in and about the region before power is of any use? It is questions of this kind which confront the executive responsible for carrying out a scheme of regional improvement; and it is with the analysis and estimation of factors of this kind that operational research is concerned.

Let us examine the steps which would actually be taken by an operational research worker confronted with a new problem. Suppose the executive authority for whom he is working has, in effect, said to him, 'What ought to be done about X?' Considerable practical experience has taught me that the first thing the scientist has to do in such circumstances is to face up to a problem which may sound rather paradoxical; he has to discover what it is that he ought to try to find out. Before he starts investigating anything, he should arrive at some opinion of what is worth investigating. It is surprising how often the importance of this stage is forgotten by those who have had little experience of delivering the scientific goods to an overworked practical man.

It is also surprising how difficult the problem may be to solve. It must be tackled from two angles. Firstly, one may ask, in a rather abstract way, what is the objective which the executive is trying to achieve? Again, in my experience, it is scarcely ever simple to answer this, at least in terms which are sufficiently down-to-earth to lead on to a useful analysis. Even in war it was not easy, although we all had in front of us the straightforward overall objective of winning the war. But was Coastal Command trying to prevent U-Boats sinking our ships, or itself to sink U-Boats? Was Bomber Command trying to disrupt industrial production or transport, or to obliterate living accommodation, or to attract the enemy's military efforts away from the fronts into the interior of the country? In peace-time, even the overall aim may be more obscure. Is a modern Agricultural Administration in a developing country trying to raise production for subsistence living, or to produce a surplus, exportable locally or overseas, to preserve the old ways of life or to facilitate the arising of a modern industrial society?

Often, perhaps usually in peace-time, the objectives are multiple; and one is trying to do several things at once. And the answer may depend, partly at least, on political considerations which the scientist is not likely to be in a good position to assess. But it is surprising how often the decision on objectives involves quantitative or even mathematical considerations, where the scientific analysis may be of real assistance. To take a simple case, it was easy to work out mathematically what would happen if Coastal Command concentrated on merely protecting ships against U-Boats and not on sinking them: the number of U-Boats available to the enemy would increase at a roughly known rate, and correspondingly the task of defending convoys against them would call for more aircraft; and a little figuring, even if it was only very roughly accurate, sufficed to show that such a policy could not work out in the long run.

One can make a similar approach in other problems. My laboratory was started after the war, part of it being financed by the Agricultural Research Council with the general aim of studying the scientific basis of animal breeding. Among my staff were two of my old Operational Research colleagues. The first thing they did was to try to make clear to themselves what animal breeders, and in particular dairy cattle breeders, are trying to do. Are they, for instance, trying to breed cows which produce more milk per lactation, or cattle which live longer and go through more lactations? They set up a long algebraic formula, which had on the one side letters representing the various items of costs, such as overheads, maintenance rations, production rations, rearing costs for replacements, etc.; and on the other items of income, from the sale of milk or of male calves or surplus heifers. Then some rather rough and ready figures were substituted for the letters and the conclusion immediately stood out that the practically possible increases in milk production per lactation were much more economically important than any probable increases in length of life. (It must be remembered that this conclusion relates to dairy cattle in Great Britain in recent years; whether it is also true elsewhere is another story.) According to their figures, an addition of one extra lactation to the average productive life of a cow was equivalent in profits to the farmer of an increase in yield per lactation of only thirty-five gallons.

This example of trying to define an objective involved finding quantitative estimates for some of the factors concerned, such as the various items of cost and income. It shows, therefore, how the attempt to clarify the aim of the executive is in practice inextricably involved with the second approach which, as I said above, the scientist has to make to his primary task of discovering what he ought to investigate. This other approach, which I have separated from the first and placed second, more for convenience of exposition than because it is less important, is to obtain a broad, general, but as far as possible quantitative, picture of what the situation is at the present time. Very often, as soon as one starts to put down in hard figures what is going on, something or other leaps to the eye as requiring attention.

I will again give an example from our work on dairy cattle. We were in this project actually confronted to begin with by another problem which most operational research workers are, one hopes, lucky enough to escape; namely to decide, not only what our executive authority wanted to do, but who he was. Were we serving the Ministry, or individual farmers, or whom? Without attempting any final solution, we took it that some of the most important executives in the field are those who run Artificial Insemination Centres, and that we might as well start by trying to be helpful to them in their attempts to bring about genetic improvement of the cattle served. Therefore the step considered in the last paragraph consisted in forming a broad but quantitative picture of what sort of success they were having in this endeavour at the time. As soon as the figures were collected, it became apparent that the success was less than had been hoped; and an important problem therefore immediately presented itself.

The collection of the figures was not entirely easy. We had in some cases to provide our own man to ensure that the necessary records were kept. This brings one to the second major factor in operational research. After deciding what you wish to find out, insist on getting hard factual evidence, in the form of objective measurements or records, and refuse to be put off with guesses or judgements even by the most experienced.

During the war I remember the fiercest controversies among staff officers of the Air Force as to the accuracy with which bombs could be aimed at submarines; it was the scientists who insisted that the aircraft must be fitted with cameras which would record objectively what actually happens, and it was by means of these records that enormously improved bombing procedures were worked out.

It is, perhaps, in this insistence on getting hold of objective, detailed facts about what is happening that operational research differs most profoundly from the methods of non-scientific administration. It is true that most enterprises record some facts about themselves, but in the first place such facts are often confined to the obviously financial, which are only a small part of the data which may be important. It is only in the last few years, for instance, that more than a small fraction of dairy farmers have troubled to record the milk yields of their individual cows. And, secondly, facts even if recorded may be left unused. They are not only laborious to collect, but it is often an even more time-consuming and boring task to analyse them and extract any general meaning from the mass of detail. Sometimes the collection of data can be simplified by using some system of sampling, but even so, a hard core of drudgery is almost certain to remain, as it does in all scientific work. Operational research workers must not be afraid to tackle it.

Having decided what to investigate, and sketched out a general picture of the existing situation, the next step is to try to find ways of improving present practice. Broadly speaking, there are two different methods of setting about the task; they were first clearly distinguished by Blackett in a paper written for the guidance of operational research workers during the war. The first he called the 'model' method. One can try to formulate a theory which takes account of all the relevant factors; and, in terms of that theory, one should be able to deduce what are the optimum results one can hope for with the methods available, and what would be the effect of different alterations in the existing practice.

To continue with our example of dairy cattle: one can work out how large a proportion of cows in a herd must be bred from if numbers are to be kept constant (supposing that none are brought in from elsewhere, because we are really interested in the total population in the whole country); one can find out, from measurements of the existing variability, how much these breeding cows can be better than the average; one can estimate, by the methods of quantitative genetics, how much of their superiority is likely to be hereditary rather than the result of a favourable environment; and performing another similar set of calculations for the small number of cows selected to breed bulls, one can finish up with an estimate (not very accurate, but serviceable) of the maximum rate of genetic improvement which can be made in a closed herd of cattle if their numbers are kept up and their mortality rates, etc., are those reigning today in Britain. This gives a definite quantitative picture from which one can see if there are any 'soft spots', where some practical procedure could produce large results. As might be expected, it is the comparatively intense selection which can be exerted on the cows used to breed bulls which turns out to be the key point to attack; and the introduction of artificial insemination offers the possibility not only of using a small number of bulls, bred from even more highly selected dams, but of progeny-testing them adequately before using them widely, so that one can mitigate the uncertainty as to how much of their dam's superiority was really genetic.

Many practical situations are, however, too complicated to be reduced to any sort of useful formula; or they may involve factors (such as 'morale') which we cannot as yet measure. On them one can try the 'variational' method. One tries to group the results of past operations in such a way that each group differs from another in that only one variable has been altered. One would use this method, for instance, to assess the value of milking three times as opposed to twice a day. But it is not always easy to find just the data which one wants, and if special procedures are introduced in order to provide comparisons with one factor altered, it may be difficult to bring to an end those which prove less successful. But in spite of its difficulties, the method may be the only one which is possible at all in a highly complicated situation, and one may have to use it as best one can while at the same time attempting to obtain a clearer theoretical picture of the matter.

By one or other, or by a combination of both these methods, the operational research worker attempts to reach conclusions which can be helpful to the executive he is serving. He must then, of course, persuade the executive of the value of his contribution, another task on which much might be written; but this is perhaps not the place for it, except to state that in my experience any argument that leads to conclusions which are practically important can be stated simply, though it may take several weeks' hard thought to discover how to do so.

Suppose then that the scientist has found out something of use, and has persuaded the executive to adopt this suggestion (even if only on a small scale at first); the operational research project is even then not finished. A stage begins which is scientifically absolutely essential, though by no means always recognized in conventional administration. One must check whether the result of the suggestion is in practice what it was expected to be, or reasonably near it. In fact it very rarely is, because other factors are likely to have changed as well as the particular point which was consciously altered on the scientist's suggestion. But at least one can usually tell whether one has done good or bad, and derive a rough idea of the magnitude of the improvement, if one has been produced.

This step of insisting on a factual check of the results of a new practice is absolutely essential if any further progress is to be made. It corresponds, of course, to the normal scientific procedure of not merely formulating a theory but then carrying out experiments to see if it works. It is, in my opinion, one of the major weaknesses of most conventional administration that it either fails to carry out such checks at all, or at least gives little weight to them. Particularly in government circles, a good administrator is too often merely the man who can put into operation some large scheme of reform, quite without reference to whether the scheme turns out to be successful or not. In old-fashioned competitive business the bank balance eventually acted as a crude automatic check; but there are nowadays enormous fields of endeavour for which that does not hold. In such circumstances, scientific checking of the results of policy must almost inevitably be introduced in the course of time; and it may well be that it is first in this connection that operational research methods will be adopted by many authorities who at first doubt their value as aids before action is taken. In any attempts to control the man-made future it is of crucial importance that adequate organizations are set up to investigate in the broadest possible contexts the detailed facts about the actual results that various policies and executive actions really produce. So far, such organizations are conspicuous only by their absence.

# 11   Technological Forecasting

One result of the new interest in the future has been the development of a number of systematic, semi-scientific and intuitive techniques for forecasting the future. Jansch's report (*Technological Forecasting in Perspective*, 1967) indentified about a hundred different techniques of forecasting – many of them recently invented. Nigel Calder, in his book *Technopolis* (1969), reports 'at the time of Jantsch's report these techniques had at best only a mild effect on the quality of forecasts, most of which continued to be made in a pragmatic, intuitive way'. He continues, 'forecasting is inevitably an art rather than a science, even though computers and other fancy techniques are already being applied to it, especially in the United States; these may give spurious authority to what are essentially hunches'.

Of these many techniques of forecasting, two main types may be distinguished – these are called *exploratory* and *normative*.

## A. Exploratory Forecasting

present

possible
future
events
or situations

*a*    *b*    *c*    *d*    *e*    *f*    *g*

Fig. 11a.1

In exploratory forecasting, the forecaster attempts to explore by examination of and extrapolation from the present, the possible future

198

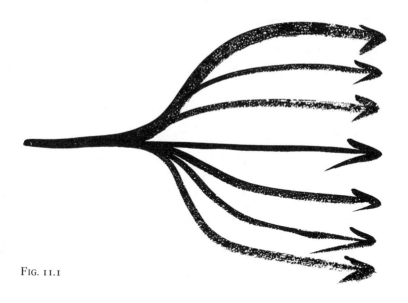

FIG. 11.1

states of any particular situation. An exploratory forecast might examine
the possible future states of an entire nation, of a city transport system,
of kitchens, of electronic components, or whatever. For example, exploratory forecasts indicate that in Europe the ownership of private cars
is rapidly increasing. There are long-term plans for the building of more
highways; and other forecasts indicate that a number of novel, urban
public transport systems are likely to be operational in the future. So,
possible future states of transport, in a European city by 1990, may be
almost entirely dependent on private cars and highways; may be mainly
dependent on new public transport systems; or it may be some mixture
of the two. There are a number of possible alternative future patterns in
urban transport to choose from. What actually happens will be the result
of a number of factors: political choices and pressures, how practical the
new transport systems turn out to be, the importance placed on environmental standards, and a multitude of other factors. The further one
looks into the future, the larger is the number of *possible alternative
futures* to choose from, and the less likely the forecaster is to be able to
predict the *actual outcome*, unless he is able to predict which of the
alternatives are actually chosen in the political arena.

   Exploratory forecasts, therefore, are useful in mapping out the
choices which are available to planners and decision-makers, given

existing technology, population, income, social patterns, etc., and their likely future development.

Exploratory forecasting techniques may be divided into three classes which indicate their use. (Note: the italicized techniques may also be used in normative forecasting.)

(a) Techniques for improving intuitive forecasts of possible futures:
these include: brainstorming, *Delphi* and *Cross-Impact Matrices*.

(b) Techniques for structuring and processing existing technological information:
these include: *scenario writing*, operational modelling, *gaming-simulation*.

(c) Techniques for generating new technological information:
these include: trend-curve extrapolation, and morphological analysis.

Consider these techniques in turn:

*Brainstorming*

Brainstorming is a technique for rapidly producing a large number of ideas on a particular problem or question from a small group of people, on the hypothesis that at least a few useful ideas will be produced. In its usual form, a brainstorming group of three to nine people are given a problem such as 'How can road accidents be reduced?' The members then record ideas on index cards as they come into their heads and also read the idea out to the group. No idea, however wild it may seem, is discussed or criticized. The idea of one member of the group usually stimulates ideas in the other members. The sort of ideas which may be produced in answer to the above question are: 'rubber vehicles', 'sticky road', 'automatic transport', 'don't travel so much', 'eliminate "T" junctions', 'magnetically repelling vehicles', etc. At the end of a brainstorming session, all the ideas may be classified by one person to give some structure to the total output of the group. For example, the main classes in the road accident ideas might include, 'reduce severity of crashes', 'automatic control', 'reduce need to travel', etc.

Brainstorming is not so much a forecasting technique as a means of generating a large number of possible solutions and ideas related to a particular problem, and is not used widely by forecasters. Brainstorming has the advantage that it can be conducted very quickly. A brainstorming session usually takes from twenty minutes to half an hour, and may be used to rapidly cover a field of interest prior to more rigorous forecasts being made.

## Delphi Technique

Perhaps the most obvious way of obtaining a forecast of long-term future developments in any particular field of study is to ask the intuitive opinion of experts in that field. A major problem is that to the same question the experts will probably give a wide range of predictions. If a number of experts were brought together to discuss when a particular development would occur, it is likely that a false consensus or discensus of opinion might be reached due to social pressures, undue influence of one expert upon another, personal disagreements and so on. The Delphi Technique, developed by Dalkey and Helmer in the early 1960s, has the object of obtaining a consensus of intuitive judgement of experts on possible future developments in various fields (science, technology, population growth, etc.) and of the most likely dates of the occurrence of these developments. In order to obtain this consensus of expert opinion, the usual method is to conduct a poll by letter among selected experts in, say, computer science, asking what developments and breakthroughs are required and likely to be realized in, say, the next thirty years. By conducting the poll by post, the disadvantages of personal conflict are avoided. One predicted development in computer science might be 'automatic interpretation of medical symptoms'. The list of developments is then sent to each participant, who is asked to make an estimate when each has a 50 per cent probability of occurring. In our example, of automatic diagnosis, one expert might put the date at between 1978 and 1986; another between 1986 and 1997. The results are plotted to show the range of opinions and fed back to the participants, who are asked to revise their estimates. Again, results are plotted and fed back for reappraisal, if no consensus on a particular development has been reached. Generally, Delphi studies have resulted in a narrowing down of the divergence of the opinions of the first poll for most developments, although an unreconcilable spread of opinions usually remains for more controversial developments.

With Delphi, as with all exploratory forecasting techniques, the further one looks into the future, the wider the spread of results. Delphi is probably most useful for making predictions in relatively narrow, highly specialized fields of study and is probably not so suitable for forecasts of broad social changes, as there are no easily recognizable experts in this sort of field.


*Cross-Impact Matrices*

The outputs of Delphi and other forecasts are often only lists of isolated possible future events, perhaps considered against a background situation such as an advanced industrial nation. However, the list might include events which are mutually exclusive or events for which chances of occurrence of some items might be influenced by the occurrence or non-occurrence of others. Cross-Impact Matrices, developed very recently, are intended to take account of the interacting effects of one change upon another. The method is described fully by Gordon and Hayward (1968). The object of conducting a Cross-Impact Matrix analysis is to generate a set of possible future events in which the effect of each event on every other event on the list has been calculated. From this list of events an internally consistent picture of the future (a futures scenario) may then be built up. The method is perhaps best illustrated by simple example. Below is a Cross-Impact Matrix showing the interactions between three possible future developments affecting urban transport.

The *individual probabilities* of the above three events, A, B, C, occurring by 1980 might be estimated in a Delphi forecast as, say, 0·9, 0·3 and 0·8. The matrix shows, however, that the probability of the mass production of low-pollution cars is increased (+) by air pollution legislation, but reduced (−) by the demonstration of a pollution-free personal public transport system. The demonstration of the public transport system is, however, substantially unaffected (o) by the production of low-pollution cars. The effects of one event on another will be dependent also upon the relative time of occurrence of each. For example, if pollution legislation appeared in 1975, this would be a stronger stimulus to the development of low-pollution cars for production in 1980 than if it was just rumoured but did not actually appear until the 1980s.

It was pointed out earlier that mathematical analysis, such as using Cross-Impact Matrices, can give spurious importance to what is chiefly only intuitive guesswork; however, it should be pointed out that such mathematical techniques offer perhaps the only means of explicitly taking account of the interacting effects between a very large number of variables in a way that cannot be done intuitively. Too much signifi-cance, however, should not be placed on *small changes* in probability of the occurrence of a particular event. Such an analysis can only hope to usefully show *gross changes* in probabilities caused by interactions be-tween events.

Cross-Impact analysis can also be used in a purely empirical way to consider interactions between events in order to build up a consistent picture of the future. A forecaster may use matrices to systematically consider the interactions between a list of possible future events in order to determine how one may impact upon another and also possibly as a means of generating side-effects. For example, forecasts indicate that world population is increasing and that new-food-production techniques are being developed. The population increase will act as a stimulus to the production of new foods and similarly this production of new foods is likely to act as a stimulus to increasing population, where hunger is staved off for a bit longer. Increasing the number of people on the earth will of course also lead to a whole variety of other side effects such as greater over-crowding, increased probabilities of international conflicts, etc.

*Scenario Writing*

Scenario writing is a technique in which the writer attempts to set up a logical series of events in order to show how, starting from the present (or any other given situation), a future situation may evolve step by step. The purpose is not to predict the future but to generate plausible future situations. So far it has primarily been applied to the exploration of potential military or diplomatic crises, particularly by Herman Kahn, as by the following example which is taken from *The Year 2000*, by Kahn and Wiener (1967):

A central European outbreak scenario. The following steps occur:

1. Unrest, precipitating incident of violence in East Germany or Berlin.
2. High level of popular agitation with street violence occurs in East Germany.
3. The East-West border, or the Berlin Wall, is opened up at various points by East German insurgents.
4. There is a limited but important degree of intervention by West German volunteers.
5. The Soviets deliver a warning to West Germany and NATO.

... And so it continues step by step. Each step being a possible outcome of the previous one.

This technique is useful in forcing a political analyst to explore some

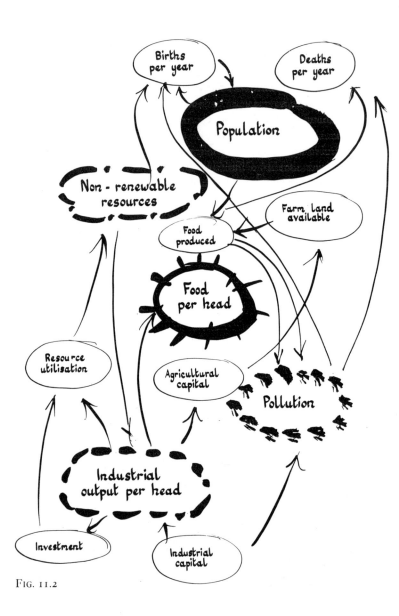

FIG. 11.2

of the possible developments of a particular crisis and thus enable him to pre-plan how more serious consequences may be averted if a similar real-world crisis occurred. Alternatively, of course, it could be used to plan how to retaliate most effectively.

Scenario writing is also being used to construct a number of possible social and technological future situations. Consider the following scenario for city traffic written by Bouladon (1967):

The last buses (electric, of course, because of the anti-pollution laws of about 1980) will have disappeared about 1990. Labor costs will have come to represent 90% of the operating cost of buses, which will still be plagued by strikes of the dissatisfied drivers. Buses will finally become too heavy and cumbersome to be able to be integrated into the centrally and electronically-guided traffic flow which will gradually extend to all the main arteries, and, by reducing the distance between electric cars to less than three meters, will increase the flow by a factor of 4.

Most ground level traffic will, however, be represented by small electric cars, cubic in shape. The urban branch of the car will have terminated its evolution and adopted the simplest most functional shape: that of a smooth plastic cube with no chromium plating and no protuberances, but standard rounded corners to facilitate handling and storing. The length of the cars will also be standardized to make them easily transportable in standardized containers. These silent, efficient cubes will have helped town-dwellers forget the noisy, evil smelling vehicles that proliferate today. They will be propelled by high-speed electric motors running at 35,000 RPM using alternating current without brushes or commutators. They will be fed at variable frequency by miniaturized thyristors. Transmission will still be necessary to convey the power to the microwheels. But such progress will have been made in construction materials that it will be possible to drive the wheels by a single-gear ratio with an efficiency of over 95%. These successors to gears will be flexible, deformable and practically everlasting.

Even town cars will not for the most part belong to their users but will be rented. Self-service taxi cabs will be made available after legislation to reduce urban congestions.

The average town-dweller, when he leaves his office, will go to the nearest 'linear-mobile park'. The latter will be situated along the main arteries (ordinary parking will not be allowed). Self-service taxi cabs, the supply of which will be computer controlled, will be hooked magnetically onto a conveyor chain under the pavement, forming a slow procession as they await customers. The traveler will insert his credit card, made of magnetized plastic, into the appropriate slot and will be able to open the car door and sit at the steering wheel. Pressure on the accelerator will release his car from the conveyor.

If he is going to the suburbs, he will be able to drive himself, but if he is going to the university and has to cross the town via the main thoroughfares, he will have to integrate into the automatic driving system, after indicating his destination by word of mouth to the central computer. On arrival he will park his car in the nearest 'linear-mobile park'.

This particular scenario, which is a fairly typical view of city traffic around 1995, is not as plausible as it could be, because the writer, possibly for lack of space in a journal article, has not given much detail of how the transport system of hired cubic cars and self-service taxi cabs has evolved. He merely gives some reasons why buses have disappeared and hints that the anti-pollution laws and legislation led to self-service taxi cabs. It is however useful as a source of technological and design ideas, although in fact many of them are not backed up by good design reasons. Standard cubic town cars may appear as either a logical or a horrifying step, depending upon your outlook; but one may ask why a single-size module? Is it intended for one, two or four people? Can it carry goods or luggage? What if a family of six, with luggage, wanted to travel together? Perhaps a better answer is various size town cars or ones which will link together. This would have to be decided by user trials to pre-test various designs, as well as considerations of economic and technical feasibility (and not merely some planner's dream of uniformity and order). Despite this sort of design criticism, which may be levelled at many scenarios depicting future worlds, this particular scenario gives useful concepts of modular vehicles, vehicle carriers, renting rather than owning, self-service taxis, linear-mobile park, magnetic credit cards to operate vehicles, dual mode cars (driver or computer controlled), oral input to control computer.

The exercise of writing a step-by-step evolutionary scenario can be very helpful in making a convincing case for the practical possibility of a futuristic development and for clarifying the writer's own ideas about how it may come about.

*Models – Operational*

When faced with the problem of exploring the possible ways in which some situation might evolve in the future, one of the most highly developed tools that an analyst has is to set up an analogue of the real world which may then be manipulated to discover how it works under new conditions. This analogue or *model* represents, in a simplified form, the processes of some aspect of the real world, such as the movement of people in the city or a political conflict. Operating the model by manipulation of its elements by means of humans, computers, or both, in order to see how it reacts (and by analogy how the real world should react), is termed *simulation*.

There are many types of operational model: mathematical, physical and gaming models are three. Which type is appropriate for the investigation of any particular situation depends on how much is known about the real-world situation and how much simplification of the real world is considered acceptable. In addition, consideration of the resources of time, skill and money available for building the model should be made.

Models may be used to describe a situation at a given point in time. These are called *descriptive models*. Or, if they contain time-dependent variables, they may be used to predict what happens at some future time. These are called *predictive models*. Manipulation of the variables in a model, or simulation, is intended to provide answers to the critical question, *'What would happen if . . .'*

Below is a brief description of the main types of models:

*Models – Mathematical*

If a lot is already known about how the system under investigation operates, or if a highly simplified model of a little-understood system is acceptable, it may be possible to devise a model comprising sets of equations to represent the system.

For example, a simple equation which has been found by experience to quite accurately describe the flow of traffic between two places, in terms of their sizes and distance apart is:

$$T_{ij} = \frac{kP_i P_j}{d_{ij}}$$

Where $T_{ij}$ = the number of journeys between place i and place j; k = a constant, $P_i$ = the population or size of i; $P_j$ = population or size of j; $d_{ij}$ = the distance, time or cost of travel between i and j; n = a constant, usually between 1 and 3.

Of course such a simple equation cannot possibly describe accurately as complex a system as traffic flow between two places. To include more of the variables which will affect the system, such as residential density, social class, income levels, transport modes available, etc., will involve much more complex equations. In addition, operating the model necessitates obtaining *numerical values*, or at least a range of probabilistic values, for all the variables involved, which, for some variables, like social class, may be estimated empirically. Some large-scale models are very complex indeed. For example, one particular economic model contains 400 equations and requires very powerful computers to handle it.

The effort of building such models is very high. Jantsch (1967), p. 200, reports that 'most models require two to three years work and cost between $50,000 and $100,000 to develop'.

Mathematical models of social and technological systems are normally only suitable for determining mass effects involving large populations, such as the demand for a transport system. Indeed, predicting measures such as demands, sales, number of votes, etc., is the main use of the mathematical models. Of course measurements of demand for some facility are dependent upon variables such as human preferences and the oddities of individual behaviour. Mathematical models and computer simulations of human behaviour have been developed and applied, apparently with reasonable success, to the prediction of voting behaviour in American presidential elections. Such models are based on empirical rules of human behaviour, drawn from common experience and experimental psychology. For example, one of the rules is: 'if A uses an argument talking to B, and persuades B, then A will not forget the argument, but B is quite likely to forget it.' Another rule is, 'if a person who is undecided on an issue hears a controversial speech on it, he is unlikely to remember it, but is likely to believe it and the speech is likely to change his attitude.' DeSola Pool (1964) argues that by including empirical principles of human behaviour in mathematical models of traffic systems, information systems, etc., and simulating using a computer capable of handling many variables simultaneously, accurate predictions of how people would react in a future situation may be obtained. Beer (1966), however, argues that although the scientific analyst using techniques of multi-variate analysis and powerful computers is *theoretically capable* of handling the very large numbers of variables involved in a real-world situation, such techniques rest on the assumption that the variables which are important may be identified.

Beer says:

Now, the kinds of system under construction (industrial operations) exhibit literally billions of variables. There is no *rigorous* means of knowing which 'matter'. Indeed, the importance of a particular variable in such a system is a question of degree, a question of judgment, a question of convention. Moreover, the importance it has by any of these criteria, change from moment to moment. This does not mean merely the numerical value assumed by the variable is changing – that is in the nature of variables, one of the things about the system that we know how to handle. No, it means more: the *structural relevance* of the variable inside the system is changing with time.

The hope that DeSola Pool expressed, of extending his analysis of human preferences from the much simpler agree-disagree voting situation to predicting human behaviour in traffic systems, etc., at least by the technique he proposes, seems unlikely to offer much valid information for planning such new systems.

*Models – Physical*

When attempting to predict the performance of a real-world system, it is sometimes possible to build a physical model of the system which can then be subjected to a variety of conditions. Well-known examples of physical models are wind-tunnel models of aeroplane wings, scale models of ships for tank testing, and scale models of buildings for structural testing. From the performance of a scale wind-tunnel model of an aircraft, the aerodynamic performance of the full-size aircraft may be predicted fairly accurately. Of course, physical models can only be built for a few situations and have limited application in long-range forecasting and planning.

Physical modelling is a highly skilled business. It is by no means always the case that the properties one is interested in will be the same in a real-life object and in an exact scale model of it, with all the linear dimensions reduced by a factor of ten or 100. Its different properties may be related to the linear dimensions in different ways. A well-known example concerns the sizes of animals. The weight increase is roughly the cube of their linear dimension, whereas the strength of their bones increases only by the square, thus one could not construct an animal built like a horse with the weight of an elephant; the strength of its leg bones would not support it. The whole question of when it is appropriate simply to scale up or down the physical model of an entity, and what to do about it when a simple enlargement or reduction of the scale is not appropriate, has been the subject of a lot of refined mathematical analysis. This is, however, not particularly relevant to our purposes here.

*Gaming-Simulation*

Whereas a mathematical model represented a situation in terms of equations suitable for manipulation by a computer, a technique called gaming, or role-playing, models the situation by means of interacting human players in a 'simulated environment' of rules, chance events, game boards and sometimes also mathematical models. The technique is a combination of analytical and experimental methods.

The longest established gaming-simulations are war games, which have been used for many hundreds of years. Recently, they have been used by military strategists to predict the outcomes of alternative strategies in simulated battles. In its simplest form a war game may consist of two opposing players (commanders) each with a certain force of troops, weapons, etc., represented by game pieces, which may be moved over a battle area according to a set of simple rules. The outcome of each move is also determined by a set of rules and is fed back to each commander. Each commander takes turn to move in response to the previous move. Each 'round' (move response), of the simulation represents the passage of, say, five hours of real time. In a slightly more sophisticated simulation, 'chance' events which might affect one side or the other (e.g. 'ammunition dump blown up by commandos' or 'thick fog') are inserted at random into the situation by a game controller and the decision makers have to respond accordingly. In even more sophisticated games, the environment is simulated as realistically as possible by highly complex and probabilistic rules enforced by a team of game operators; whole teams of opposing players may be involved; and the consequences of a move may be calculated by means of a probabilistic mathematical model which may take into account the terrain, morale, the type of weapons, the weather, etc., all operated by computer.

One of the main uses of war games is to simulate hypothetical future conflict situations in which one side has a new weapon, with given characteristics, or has adopted some new strategy. By means of several replications of the simulation, some consistent pattern of the outcomes of the conflict may be established. Another important use of war gaming is to train commanders in a situation in which the consequences of any mistakes are not disastrous.

As well as for the simulation of battles, gaming has been adopted to simulate a wide range of other situations for the purposes of training the participants, to gain some insight into the workings of the situation, or to discover the effects of various strategies of play. The main types are: international-relations games, for the simulation of diplomatic crises; business games, for the simulation of management decision-making; planning games, for the simulation of the town-planning process; and educational games, for simulating a very wide variety of situations specifically for teaching purposes.

The elements of each type of game are similar – conflicting and cooperating players taking on roles, e.g. a town-planning game may include roles of planner, house developer, local residents, shop-keepers, factory manager, etc.; and a simulated environment. In an international-relations game, this environment may simply be an introductory scenario describing the situation (an international crisis) to the players (representing the interests of the nations involved), who are located in different rooms (representing the nations). Procedures through which players may communicate (e.g. diplomatic messages, newspaper reports, meetings, etc.) are usually used during the simulation. Alternatively, the environment may be, as in a business game, a computer simulation of the market, which calculates the consequences (e.g. the effects on sales of investments, etc.) of each decision made by the players.

The value of gaming-simulation as a teaching tool is fairly well established, particularly for management trainees. Its value as a research method is not so well established, being dependent upon the complex question of the validity of the simulation as an analogue of the real world. Gaming has the following merits – a hypothetical future or past environment may be brought into the present for investigation. In theory, almost anything may be made to 'occur' during a simulation. Decision-making is performed by people who will include all their biases, irrationality, value judgements, which characterize real-world decisions. Time may be speeded up or slowed down, so that several days, weeks or years may be simulated in one hour.

Although gaming-simulation has been recognized as a potentially very useful method of exploring possible future situations, its applications beyond the exploration of hypothetical future and diplomatic situations have been few. Gordon and Helmer have developed a 'Future' game for the Kaiser Aluminum and Chemical Corporation in which the probabilities of possible future events (relevant mainly to the Western countries), such as 'staggered work week replaces Monday through Friday standard' and 'computerized medical diagnosis is in wide use', are influenced by interactions between events, the wishes of the players and chance. Charles Osgood has explored, at the University of Illinois, through Project PLATO, the possibilities of using computers and teaching machines to make available complex sets of branching choices leading to alternative futures. A description of this project is to be found in Jungk and Galtung (1969). Arthur Waskow, at the Institute for Policy Studies, Washington, who has recognized the potential of gaming-simulation for involving members of the public in exploring future worlds, aims to involve people from ghetto areas of Washington in future games. One game might involve a particular type of school system of the year 2000 – perhaps a highly automated school whose students frequently use euphoria-creating drugs, are politically organized and carry on political and social action with deprived groups in the community. Participants in this 'game' play roles of parent, student, teacher, city councillor, taxpayer, each faced with the crisis created by the sudden advent of an intelligence-enhancing drug.

Buckminster Fuller's 'World Game' is intended as both a teaching and an investigative tool. By means of graphic displays of the earth, players in the game can learn about the world's resources in the past and in the future under various conditions and can explore means of deploying the world's resources. For a description of a World Game session, see *World Game Report* by Edwin Schlossberg (1969).

*Trend Extrapolation*

Trend extrapolation is one of the longest established forecasting techniques and, as its name implies, rests on the assumption that a particular measurable trend (e.g. population, aircraft speed, number of books published, personal incomes, etc.) is likely to continue into the future following a particular trend curve, plotted from past experience.

The chief use of trend extrapolation is not so much to forecast what *will* happen, but to determine what *might* happen if the internal and external factors which produced the trend in the past remain the same during a future period. Alternatively, trend extrapolation may be used also to forecast the likely possibilities offered by some as yet undeveloped technology (e.g. the past trend in aircraft speeds indicates that certain further increases are likely in the future and that new propulsive technology would be required to reach these new speeds).

Concern over world population growth is dramatically explained by examination of world population trends over the last few thousand years, and the population projections for the next thirty years. (See 11.3.)

World population has followed an approximately exponential growth curve (this means that the period over which the world's population doubles decreases over time). The portion of the curve extrapolated from the present day over the next thirty-five years indicates that, if the main factors affecting population remain constant, world population is likely to double; whereas the previous population doubling took about fifty-five years. This trend of course logically cannot continue indefinitely and must level off at some time in the future. When this occurs cannot be forecast by extrapolation, but will depend on the interac-

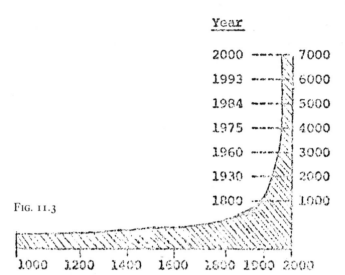

World Population Growth
and Projections

Year

| Year | | Population |
|------|---|------------|
| 2000 | | 7000 |
| 1993 | | 6000 |
| 1984 | | 5000 |
| 1975 | | 4000 |
| 1960 | | 3000 |
| 1930 | | 2000 |
| 1800 | | 1000 |

FIG. 11.3

1000   1200   1400   1600   1800   1900   2000

tions between the factors determining population growth. Figure 11.3 shows growth in world population postulated by the United Nations on the assumption that fertility would remain at the present level, that some controls will operate but fertility will remain high, and that fertility will drop significantly. For global trends having great inertia, such as world population growth, short-term (three to eight years) deviations from the trend are relatively unlikely and simple extrapolation is likely to indicate what actually happens. In the longer term, even trends with great momentum are subject to the influence of deliberate policies (e.g. birth control) and other factors (e.g. value changes, economic depression). It appears, however, that measures such as population, when viewed on a more detailed level, are highly sensitive to external factors, such as the economic climate, and that steady trends can suddenly be reversed. For example, the population of England and Wales declined consistently between 1918 and 1930. The official demographic forecast in 1930 was made on the assumption that this trend would continue or accelerate. What actually happened was that the population began to rise in 1930 and has done so steadily ever since.

Kahn and Wiener in their book, *The Year 2000*, use trend extrapolation to generate a 'surprise-free' (i.e. continuing trends) picture of the economic future. To determine the likely level of personal incomes in the future in various countries of the world they draw the best straight line through the points in the incomes against growth graph and extrapolate this line into the future. The assumption is made that no major wars or economic depressions will occur over the forecasting period.

The graph (11.4) illustrates the significantly different projections

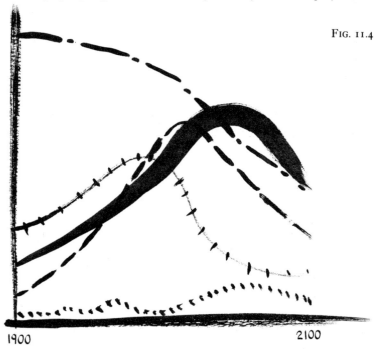

FIG. 11.4

1900                                    2100

which can result from simple extrapolation on a short-term or a long-term basis, even if assumptions of no gross external changes (economic depressions, etc.) are correct. Straight-line extrapolation through 1882 and 1966 indicates a 2000 GNP per capita of $6,500, while extrapolation through 1959 and 1966 indicates a level of $10,000.

The best way to guard against this sort of mistake is to make a large number of projections, say for a series of twenty-year periods, beginning in 1870, 1875, 1885 and so on, and then for a number of different thirty-year periods. Usually the false-projections result in the drawing of a line through bottom of a down curve to the top of an up will become obvious. There are more sophisticated mathematical ways of receiving a similar result.

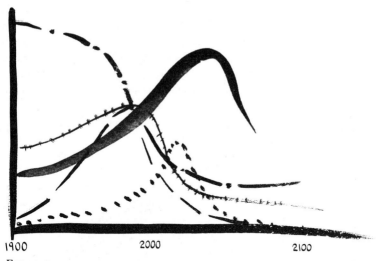

1900        2000        2100

FIG. 11.5

Jantsch (1967) identifies four main classes of trend curve (11.5).

It can be seen that all these trend curves eventually exhibit gradual or rapid change in shape (rising or flattening off). The uncertainty with trend extrapolation is when these changes will occur.

## B. Normative

Whereas exploratory forecasts are concerned with what future changes and developments are possible, normative forecasts are concerned with identifying *long-term goals* and *desirable futures* and with working out the steps by which this desirable future state may be brought about.

The norms or goals may be very simply expressed. Examples of possible goals are: 'abolition of human hunger by the year 2000', 'get a man to Mars', 'reduce air pollution to a given level by 1975', 'double the number of new houses built over the next ten years' and so on. Certain normative forecasts might also detail the organizational, social, technological and other changes necessary to realize the goal. The goal or desirable future may also be expressed in much broader, more general terms, e.g. a description of an ideal form of community, a new form of political structure, a performance specification for an urban transport system, etc.

It should be recognized that normative forecasts are essentially political or philosophical statements, i.e. the goals can only be decided by debate, agreement, dissent, etc., and cannot be verified as 'correct' in an objective way.

Also, realistic normative forecasts should mesh with the framework of possibilities predicted by exploratory forecasts. There is little value in setting goals, the achievement of which requires the realization of technological, social or organizational developments which no exploratory forecast considers achievable in the time-scale envisaged.

Many of the techniques used in exploratory forecasting are also suitable for setting goals and identifying desirable futures. Of those described, 'Delphi', scenario-writing and gaming have been or could potentially be used to generate goals and to formulate desirable future worlds. The Delphi Technique may be employed to obtain a consensus of opinions on desirable future events and, on long-range goals, scenario writing in reverse (i.e. describing some desirable future situation and specifying the steps by which this situation may come about, starting from the present), is a powerful normative method. This technique has also been termed evolutionary forecasting. Gaming offers the possibility of involving large (or small) numbers of people in the identification of desirable future events and desirable future situations (as in Gordon and Helmer's 'Game of the Future', in which each participant builds a 'World of 1986' and attempts to persuade other participants to 'invest' in his world). In addition, a few techniques specifically for the specification and evaluation of goals have been developed, the best-known being the various techniques based on relevance trees and goal hierarchies.

*Relevance Trees*

Relevance trees are hierarchically ordered networks of objectives, the main purpose of which is as an aid to decision-making in complex situations in which it may not be obvious where to allocate one's resources. A vertical relevance tree relates a long-term objective to the alternative actions that should be taken in order to achieve that objective.

The first step in the construction of a relevance tree is to identify a high-level objective that you wish to achieve at some time in the future – e.g. an overall objective may be to reduce air pollution levels.

The next step is to qualitatively relate the alternative courses of action (or the elements contributing towards the objective) to the overall objective using exploratory forecasting techniques when necessary. Below is a portion of a vertical relevance tree for air pollution.

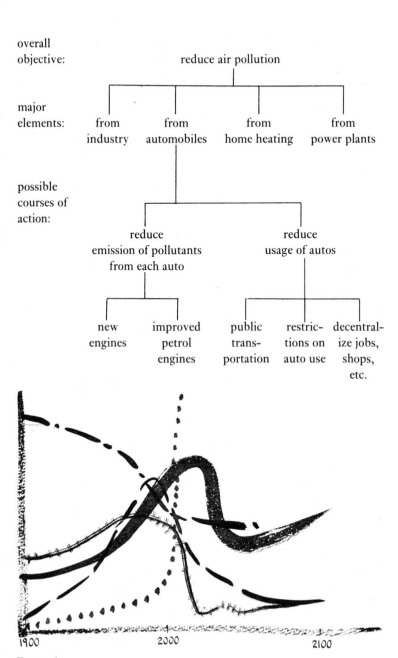

overall
objective:                              reduce air pollution

major
elements:        from            from              from              from
              industry      automobiles    home heating    power plants

possible
courses of
action:
                        reduce                          reduce
               emission of pollutants           usage of autos
                  from each auto

                new       improved        public      restric-   decentral-
              engines       petrol        trans-      tions on   ize jobs,
                           engines      portation    auto use     shops,
                                                                    etc.

1900                          2000                      2100

FIG. 11.6

217

The tree is continued down to a level where practical inputs feed in (e.g. particular research and development, legal measures, etc.). One of the possible low-level inputs might be research on cheap, high-capacity batteries for electric vehicles.

This form of hierarchical network specifies the alternative paths by which the overall goal may be achieved. Technical economic, social and other forecasts and feasibility studies may then be made to determine which of the paths are most likely to lead to the realization of the goal in the desired time.

The Planning–Programming–Budgeting System (or PPBS) is based on another form of hierarchical network, sometimes called a horizontal relevance tree. PPBS has been used in the US Defense Department since 1961 and in civilian departments since 1965. Once again the object is to relate the elements of a particular area of interest to a high-level goal to obtain a framework for decision-making and medium-range planning. The difference is, then, that instead of specifying alternative paths for achieving the goal, the tree should include all the elements necessary to achieve it.

The first step in PPBS is to set up a function-oriented relevance tree. Below is a hypothetical example (from Jantsch, 1967):

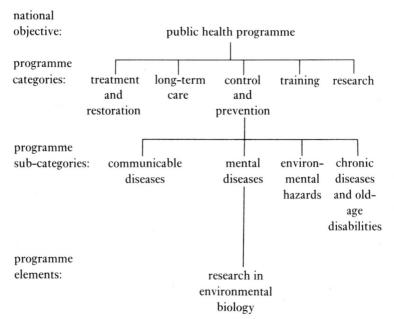

national objective: public health programme

programme categories: treatment and restoration | long-term care | control and prevention | training | research

programme sub-categories: communicable diseases | mental diseases | environmental hazards | chronic diseases and old-age disabilities

programme elements: research in environmental biology

The relevance tree does not of itself solve any problems. However, it may be used as a framework for guiding the major part of the analysis, using techniques such as cost-effectiveness, systems analysis, operations research, in order to make decisions on the most effective allocation of resources at the input (lowest) levels in order to reach the high-level objective.

*Pattern*

The relevance tree concept has been used as a basis for a sophisticated quantitative method for policy-making and planning developed by the military and space science department of Honeywell, Inc. The method was named PATTERN (Planning Assistance Through Technical Evaluation of Relevance Numbers) and has been used particularly in medical, space and military planning. A full description of the method may be found in Esch (1969).

To apply the PATTERN scheme, it is first necessary to draw up a relevance tree. This consists of a series of levels, on each of which there are a number of items. All the items on any one level are relevant, in some degree or other, to each of the items on the level above. The topmost level consists of the ultimate objectives of the exercise being examined; on the level immediately below are a number of subordinate criteria qualifying those objectives; below that is a level of sub-subordinate criteria, and so on, down to the lowest level, which is that of the detailed tactical inputs into the system. Numerical estimates have to be given for the relevance, or 'significance number' $s$, of each item on the $n$ th the level for each item on the $n - 1$ th level. We thus have to handle a large number of coefficients, which may be written in the general form $s_{j(n)}^{i(n-1)}$. Assigning these coefficients is, of course, the most difficult part of the task of setting up a PATTERN. Honeywell is said to have used twenty experts for six months to set up its basic PATTERN for military and space developments. I will return later to how this part of the job is carried out.

It may make matters clearer at this point to give an example of a PATTERN applied to a university situation. To simplify I shall carry the tree only down to the level of Departments, and shall concentrate on those related to the Faculty of Science.

We first draw up a relevance tree, showing the various levels which are believed to be important. I have taken it that the top level, the output which is the goal of the whole exercise, is number of graduates produced. In the next lower level are the Faculties (or Departments) from which these graduates come; I have assumed there are five: Physics–Chemistry, Biology, Earth–Space Sciences, Mathematics, Computer Sciences. In the next level are the different kinds of graduates who have to be considered. Again I have supposed there to be five main types: academics who are going on in the university or research world; practitioners who will become professional specialists in industry, etc.; executives who will eventually go on to industrial management, sales, etc.; students who just want to become educated; and mature students who have come back to the university for a refresher course. Then, at the level labelled 'qualities', we list the different types of study; going into the subject in real depth; discovering how to find out relevant information when you need it (information retrieval); understanding of the technological revolution, which is going on in all subjects; understanding the relevance of the subject to the global society we are moving towards; and being able to be flexible in making use of information. Finally, in row five, we again list the various teaching faculties, but we shall use this row to estimate what contribution each faculty should make to producing the various sorts of graduates with the appropriate qualities.

*Levels in the Relevance Tree*

| (1) Output Goals | Numbers of Graduates | | | | |
|---|---|---|---|---|---|
| (2) 'Faculties' | Phys. Chem. | Biol. | Earth– Space | Maths | Computer Science |
| (3) 'Types' | Academic | Practitioner | Exec. | Educ. Man. | Mature Student |
| (4) 'Qualities' | Depth | Inf. Retriev. | Technol. Rev. | Global Soc. | Flexibil. |
| (5) 'Faculties Inputs' | Phys. Chem. Biol. | Earth– Space Maths. | Computer Science | Sci. Stud. | Soc. Sci. Humani- ties |

Relevance Tree for Science Subjects FIG. 11.7

We next have to put in some numbers, to indicate how many people there are in the various groups. The table deals with levels 2 and 3. The contribution of each of the Faculties to the total output of graduates is in the first column, to the left of the vertical line. In the rest of the table, each row shows the proportion of the five types of students in each Faculty. (These figures, and all those given later, are pure inventions, made up simply to provide a definite *example* of the kind of thing one might find. They are not to be taken as expressing a serious opinion.)

| Faculty | Output | Acad. | Pract. | Exec. | Educ. | Mature |
|---------|--------|-------|--------|-------|-------|--------|
| Phys. Chem | 3 | 3 | 3 | 2 | 1 | 1 | 10 |
| Biol. | 3 | 4 | 3 | 1 | 1 | 1 | 10 |
| Earth–Space | 2 | 3 | 4 | 2 | 1 | 0 | 10 |
| Maths | 1 | 5 | 2 | 2 | 1 | 0 | 10 |
| Computer Science | 1/2 | 2 | 5 | 1 | — | 2 | 10 |

Fig. 11.8

These same figures are shown graphically in the diagram below. (Fig. 11.9)

When we go to the next lowest level, 'Qualities', the complete set of tables would be rather complex, since there has to be a separate table for each Faculty. I have set out below the tables for only two Faculties, those of Physics–Chemistry and Computer Sciences. In each table, the left-hand column shows the strength of the output of that kind of graduate from that Faculty. For instance, Physics–Chemistry contributes three to the total output (table above) and of those a proportion of three will be academics; so the academics are rated as nine in the Physics–Chemistry table below.

| Phys. Chem. | | Depth | Inf. Exp. | Tech. Dev. | Glob. Sci. | Flex. |
|-------------|----|-------|-----------|-----------|-----------|-------|
| Acad. | 9 | 6 | 2 | $\frac{1}{2}$ | $\frac{1}{2}$ | 1 |
| Pract. | 9 | 3 | 3 | $\frac{1}{2}$ | $\frac{1}{2}$ | 3 |
| Exec. | 6 | 2 | 2 | 1 | 1 | 4 |
| Educ. | 6 | 2 | $\frac{1}{2}$ | $1\frac{1}{2}$ | 2 | 4 |
| Mature | 3 | 2 | 2 | 1 | 1 | 4 |
| | | 105 | $64\frac{1}{2}$ | $22\frac{1}{2}$ | 24 | 34 |

*Computer Science*

| | | | | | | |
|-------------|----|-------|-----------|-----------|-----------|-------|
| Acad. | 1 | 5 | 2 | $\frac{1}{2}$ | $\frac{1}{2}$ | 2 |
| Pract. | $2\frac{1}{2}$ | 2 | 4 | 2 | — | 2 |
| Exec. | $\frac{1}{2}$ | 2 | 2 | 2 | 1 | 3 |
| Educ. | — | — | — | — | — | — |
| Mature | 1 | 4 | 3 | — | — | 3 |
| | | 15 | 16 | $6\frac{1}{2}$ | 1 | $11\frac{1}{2}$ |

Fig. 11.9

The figures in these tables are again shown graphically below, although in the drawing I have used figures for Physics–Chemistry and Biology, instead of Computer Science.

The final step in this illustrative example is to consider the inputs which the various Faculties might make to help produce the graduates. I give only one example, in 11.10, which deals with the contributions of various Departments to the production of Physics–Chemistry graduates who are going to become executives. For this matrix we need to consider contributions from all Faculties, not only Science ones. I have, in the illustration, added only two main types, Social Sciences and Humanities. The last row of figures sums up these contributions. It is noteworthy that, according to the significance numbers assigned here, the Computer Science contribution is nearly two thirds as large as that of the parent Physics–Chemistry Department. This comes about because of the emphasis which I have placed on the importance of information-retrieval and of understanding of the contribution of computers to general technology. These judgements can, of course, well be queried.

| Inputs to Phys. Exec. | | Phys. Chem. | Biol. | Earth–Space | Maths. | Comp. | Sci. Stud. | Soc. Sci. | Humanities |
|---|---|---|---|---|---|---|---|---|---|
| Depth | 12 | 7 | — | — | 2 | 1 | — | — | — |
| Inf. Exp. | 12 | — | 1 | — | 1 | 6 | 1 | 1 | — |
| Tech. Rev. | 6 | 2 | 1 | — | — | 2 | 1 | 3 | 1 |
| Glob. Sci. | 6 | — | 1 | — | — | — | 3 | 3 | 3 |
| Flex. | 24 | 4 | 1 | — | 1 | 1 | 1 | 1 | 1 |
| | | 192 | 48 | — | 48 | 120 | 60 | 72 | 60 |

Fig. 11.10

This raises the fundamental problem; how should the significance numbers be assigned? At some points in the scheme, e.g. the output values assigned to the Faculties in the first step, there are various semi-objective criteria which can be used; for instance, projections from the actual numbers, or modifications introduced in the light of estimates of national requirements, etc. Or one can fix these values in accordance with subjective goals which have been arrived at in various ways. In general, through the bulk of the series of matrices, most of the significance values will have to be estimated by intuitive judgement, since no adequate factual data are available. This need not be so great a disadvantage, if it is realized that the usefulness of a scheme such as PAT-TERN is in the main to clarify the issues involved in attempts con-sciously to direct the development of an organism such as a university. It shows what the implications are of, say, a decision to try to produce more of the graduates I have called executives, or to provide various kinds of broader education for academic-research people, or to deal with the re-education/extended-leisure syndromes with which we seem likely to be confronted.

## C. Technology Assessment

The phrase 'technology assessment' has recently become not merely fashionable but also official; since an Office of Technology Assessment has been set up in the United States Congress, and there are plans for one in West Germany. The expression is the name for attempts to foresee the side-effects and secondary repercussions of new tech-nologies. Technological Forecasting, in the specialized sense in which that name is usually used, is concerned with trying to work out the nature and the efficiency of anticipated technological advances, in carry-ing out the primary tasks for which they might be brought into use. For instance, what are the prospects for supersonic aircraft, as a tech-nology for carrying people and things from one place to another? Technology Assessment tries to go further in two ways. Firstly, it asks, what will the secondary consequences be? In injecting substances into the stratosphere? In sonic booms? In further concentrating control over transport in the hands of a very few great industrial nations? Con-solidating the stratification of society, not just into those who travel first or second class on the same trains, but those who can fly Concorde (at the expense of their firm or government) and those who can't? And so on. And, secondly, Technological Assessment aims at making explicit comparisons between alternative technologies. How many of the worth-while uses of supersonic aircraft could be achieved (and at what cost) by development of the video-phone? Would it be more sensible for European and US businessmen to meet, not by either of them flying right across the Atlantic, putting their biological clocks out of kilter, but by both taking a leisurely trip to a floating 'conference island', set up somewhere in the doldrums of the mid-Atlantic?

It is something of an indictment of the over-specialization of our present civilization, and of its simple-minded fascination with the get-rich-quick potentials of new technologies, that anyone has had to invent a new name for the very common-sense idea of trying to think all round the consequences of innovations in technical methods. But it is probably quite useful to have a special name. I had already come across many attempts by scientists, either as individuals, or as organized groups, to think through in this way the likely, or possible, results of their work. I have known individuals who have switched out of, say, some types of microbiology because of the possibility it might turn out to be useful for biological warfare; and organizations, like the International Union of Biological Sciences, which have tried to set up 'look-out' committees which try to think out the social consequences of various types of research, e.g. on ageing, or identifying brain centres where stimulation will give sensations of great pleasure. Nearly always, the difficulty has gradually imposed itself, that such assessments are extremely difficult. It would not have been easy – maybe it would have been impossible – to foresee that Henry Ford's new technology of production-line fabrication of cars for the masses would, by providing mobile private rooms, entirely change society's ideas about acceptable sexual behaviour. But I feel that if an organized effort had been made to think round the subject, at least the *possibility* might have been foreseen, even if no one could tell whether it would actually happen or not; and that would have been a little more insight than did occur at the time. Giving this sort of normally cautious and sceptical attitude a name, Technology Assessment, may make it easier to arrange things so that the necessary hard work – which is beyond the capacity of most ordinary individuals – actually gets done, in so far as it can be.

So Technology Assessment might be called 'Technological Forecasting in the Round'. But I do not think it has developed any new methods of setting about its task which need to be described here, other than saying, let common sense rip, with no holds barred; and when you think you've thought of everything, think again and see if you can't find something else.

# 12  System Modelling

Recently there have been developments of the procedure of trying to set up a 'model' of the system mentioned on p. 212, which have become important enough to merit having a chapter to themselves. These developments have been occurring now, because computers have become powerful enough to handle models which are so complex that it would be intolerably tedious, if possible at all, to deal with them by ordinary algebra or arithmetic. If the model involves several things which interact with one another (e.g. the population, food supply, industrial equipment available, pollution produced and a few others), and particularly if the strength of the interactions does not stay constant (e.g. pollution may have little effect on the other things, until it increases above some limit, when it may begin to get more and more important), then the system may involve equations which cannot actually be solved by algebra, in the present state of the art. But still the computer, which can only do arithmetic, can do it so fantastically fast that it can slog out the answers to a complicated set of equations just by going along one short step at a time.

This sort of operation produces a lot of lovely-looking figures, which can be made into elegant graphs. The possibility of getting such results out of ideas about what the system is like, which previously it had been impractical to handle, is obviously very seductive. But letting oneself be seduced is only sometimes, unfortunately by no means always, a good thing in the long run. The results of these computer runs on models of complex systems look nice and precise, but can actually be no better than the ideas which go into them. The computer will turn out a result from a lousy model just as happily as from a good one; in fact, it can't tell the difference. The capacities of the computer are a really important and powerful new tool; but they have to be used with caution, just as much as when we get a new machine tool with performance much better than anything we have been used to. We are still only just learning how to handle the computer-tool. Some of the promises and problems of this new method of dealing with complex things will be illustrated by considering its application to perhaps the most complex problem anyone has yet tried to tackle – the present-day world as a whole going concern (if it is going?) – what the Club of Rome calls, the World Problematique.

## The World as a System

The future development of the world will obviously be affected by very many factors – population, foodstuffs, pollution, natural resources, technological developments and so on. Moreover, all of these have complicated interactions with each other. An increase in the production of power of the utilization of natural resources for industry will almost certainly tend to increase pollution. An increase in the number of people demands more food, but the provision of more foodstuffs may in the first place tend to increase the rate of population growth. We are in fact confronted with a complex system involving a highly interactive network of very many components.

At the time of writing, attempts are just being started to try to unravel the complexities of the situation and to understand its behaviour by means of computer simulations. The first tentative step in this direction was sponsored by an international group of industrialists, scientists and others calling themselves the Club of Rome and organized by an Italian industrial consultant, Aurelio Peccei. They arranged financial support for a preliminary study to be made by a computer team at the Massachusetts Institute of Technology. An outline of the method they had followed and the first results they had attained was published in a book, *The Limits to Growth*. The Club of Rome, whose members were amongst the first to realize the enormous importance of investigating the probable or possible futures of mankind, arranged that the book have wide publicity throughout the world; and it has certainly stirred up a great deal of interest even in the most official governmental circles.

If one were foolish enough to take its computer projections to be serious *predictions* of what is going to happen, they appear highly pessimistic, foretelling catastrophic events such as halving the world's population. There is still sufficient Victorian optimism around – the belief that bigger and more costly always means better – for a lot of people, even many who should have known better, to get very hot under the collar and try to bury the whole enterprise under a fog of ridicule. It is therefore important to try to get some idea of what computer simulations of complex situations cannot be expected to do in the present state of the art; and where the MIT team, and others more recently associated with the Club of Rome, have actually got to date.

The procedure in setting up a computerized model of a complex system is something like this. You start by choosing, on the basis of common sense, a certain number of major components of the system which seem likely to be of importance. The MIT study chose five main variables: population, capital expenditure, natural resources, pollution and capital investment in agriculture. Each of these is subdivided again into a lower level of active factors; such as, for population, birth-rates and death-rates; or in other sectors, such factors as the amount of arable land available, the capital cost of bringing new lands into cultivation and so on. Then one has to try to put into the model quantitative estimates of the strengths of interactions between the factors; for instance what effect has pollution on population? These interaction effects ('multipliers' in the system-builder's jargon) at present usually have to be guessed, since there are only a minimal number of facts on which to base the estimates. However, the computer is flexible enough to deal with 'multipliers' which change according to the actual values of the two things which are interacting. For instance, the MIT team suggested that pollution does not have a proportionate effect on death rates at all levels, but has very little effect until it reaches a fairly high level and then rapidly becomes more and more of a killer. This is a guess based on such phenomena as, for instance, the great London smog of the winter of 1952 which was reckoned to have precipitated the death of several thousand people.

The only real check – and it is a pretty feeble one – on the validity of these guesses is to show that the whole system produces a reasonably accurate picture of what happened to all the variables for which figures are available for some period in the past, for instance, from 1900 to 1960. Any set of interaction values which fail to do that would of course be unacceptable; but quite a lot of different values would probably produce a reasonable fit to the existing data, particularly since none of the factors which look like becoming very important in the future, such as high levels of pollution or the exhaustion of some natural resources, had yet begun to exert any important influence at that time.

Having set up the model and shown that it does at least work for the past, the computer will work out for you what would happen if the same set of interactions continued on into the future.

What happens with the MIT model is that by the end of the century the world begins to run out of natural resources and can no longer support such a large population, which gets dramatically, indeed catastrophically, reduced. The MIT team then tried the effect on the behaviour of their model of altering some of the numerical values they had fed into it. As a continuation of their original set-up would lead to an exhaustion of natural resources, an obvious step would seem to be to reduce the rate at which natural resources are exploited. When they changed the values in the model to correspond with such a new policy, what came up was an eventual rise in pollution, which again eventually led to a population catastrophe. So what about both reducing the rate of exploiting natural resources and increasing the efficiency of industry in relation to pollution production? This just postpones the catastrophe for a bit, but eventually led to the same type of result. In fact, the only alterations to the MIT model which give rise to an essentially stable situation, in which the population neither rose nor fell abruptly, was one involving severe restraints on the rates of capital investment, of resource exploitation and even of food production. To those used to everything getting continuously bigger and better it sounds like a very cheerless prospect.

How seriously should these results be taken?

As *predictions*, they should not be taken seriously at all. They do not pretend, and were not intended, to forecast what *will* happen. Their importance, which is quite real, is of a different kind, or rather of three different kinds.

In the first place they do show types of catastrophic misfortunes which *could* take place if the world went on working according to a system which is not too drastically implausible. Secondly, they drive home the lesson that if one does something to make an alteration in a complex system, the response of the system may not at all be what was expected or intended. This is a lesson which people continually have to learn over again. The behaviour of complex systems is often what the MIT team call 'counter-intuitive' – the damn thing just does not do what it *should* do. An earlier study by the same group of workers at MIT was on the growth processes in cities. It had been quite a common experience, particularly in the United States, that a well-meaning authority undertakes a programme of slum clearance, erects a lot of new, quite superior, housing, and within a few years finds that the original slum area is even more overcrowded with poorer people than before. Probably one of the main factors in causing this counter-intuitive behaviour is that the new buildings attract a large number of people into the area, but if there are not enough jobs for them, they remain poor and let their dwellings get even more overcrowded. Indeed, investigating just why the complex systems do not behave as expected is the main purpose of trying to make models of them.

A third importance of the MIT world scheme is that it is a beginning of this process of exploring a variety of models, to see if one can be produced which really behaves as the world itself does. It must be emphasized that the present world model is only a first step. Already several others have been taken to enlarge or improve it, or to try various versions of it. The general system that the MIT team has used is quite flexible, and can be modified in many different ways to obtain almost any sort of behaviour one wants to extract from it. Several people have already shown that if you make more optimistic assumptions, you will elicit more encouraging behaviour from the system. For instance, a group in Holland has shown that if you expect new natural resources to be discovered much more rapidly than the MIT group thought likely, the collapse due to exhaustion of natural resources does not occur. Again, an American author has inserted a sort of technological joker, suggesting that technology will advance fast enough to mop up all the problems, and again, of course, the system behaves in a much more stable way than the original model. There is, of course, room for a great deal of debate as to whose assumptions are the most plausible; and it is quite important to explore the whole range of modifications of the model to see which ones actually produce the kinds of development which we would hope to occur, and to which factors it is therefore most important to pay attention.

However, it is probably still more important to improve the basic causal structure of the model, as put forward in its first version. It has some very great obvious deficiencies. In the first place, it lumps conditions all over the world together in a single world-index (in technical jargon, it is highly 'aggregated'). It makes no distinction even between the rich and the poor countries; and there cannot be very much sense in summarizing the pollution conditions in all regions of the world under one single pollution index. Then another serious deficit is that it deals with only one single level of interactions; a causal level at which a certain intensity of exploitation of natural resources leads inevitably to a certain degree of pollution; and that again inevitably has a certain effect on birth-rates, death-rates and so on in the actual world. There are, of course, actually many levels, and in particular there is the level of human adaptive behaviour. If man sees that he is producing too much pollution, he may set about dealing with it, not by reducing the amount of natural resources he uses, but by decreasing the amount of pollution produced from that use. The Mark I model could be elaborated and expanded to incorporate a number of new and important features of this kind. In fact several groups around the world, associated with the Club of Rome, have begun work to do so. For instance, a South American group is developing a model which distinguishes between the poor and the rich nations, and studies the effect of interactions between them. Another group in Germany is working on a model which will divide the world into three portions, the rich, the poor and the Communist, and will also incorporate a level of 'goal-seeking' controls, which operate to try to keep the other variables within certain predetermined limits, or forces them to change in certain definite ways.

There again the MIT Mark I model, and even the Mark IIs which have been suggested, do not make adequate allowance for the periods of time essential for various developments. For instance, when we discover new deposits of natural resources, such as a new oil- or gas-field, a new deposit of some important metaliferous mineral, these cannot be instantaneously made available to the productive machiner. Harrison Brown has pointed out that the rich countries have, over the last few centuries, accumulated an enormous backing of mined, refined and processed metals, such as steel, aluminium, copper and so on. He calculates that to put behind every adult in the world the quantity of extracted and fabricated metals on which each American stands, would require that every existing mining and processing plant did nothing else for several decades, even if the population of the world remained constant; while if it increased at the rate it is increasing now, the task would take a few centuries. In the world's productive system there are in fact unavoidable lags, and any truly realistic model will have to incorporate these.

There are certainly going to be great challenges and complexities in trying to develop adequate working models of the world system. The mere effort of thinking out such models will force people to develop much clearer ideas about interaction of the many factors involved in the evolution of man's future economic and ecological situation; but it will probably be a long time before any of these models is sufficiently like the real world to provide more concrete guidance than a hint and a warning.

# Epilogue

When an author who has written a longish book reads it all through, he is almost bound to ask himself what is likely to be the reaction of someone else – who also reads it through to the end. In the case of this book, I suspect that anyone who reaches this point may feel that he has survived something of a steeplechase; he may even have had to close his eyes and skip a few of the more formidable leaps or obstacles that he has found in his path. I cannot pretend that all the ideas which I have tried to sketch in this book are easy ones. That could hardly be, since so many of them are relatively new. The point about them is that they are attempts to come to grips with a subject – the understanding of complex systems – which we have only quite recently realized is of crucial importance for how we deal with the practical affairs of the world. The ideas differ a good deal not only in difficulty but in power, and no doubt some will prove to be more useful than others. I have in many cases stated rather clearly how I myself rate some of the newer methods, but I admit I may be wrong in some of these assessments, and time may prove that I have been too critical of some approaches, and too enthusiastic about others. Again, such uncertainties are inevitable when one is dealing with ideas which have not yet been around long enough for opinion about them to have crystallized into conventional and universally accepted valuations. We have been discussing a field which is still very free and open-ended – free for people to make mistakes, as well as free for people to produce very fertile new insights.

The analogy of a steeplechase is not actually very illuminating about the nature of a book such as this. It might be better to say that it is like a manual provided for someone who had spent his whole life in the centre of a large area of solid land, like middle-west America or central Asia, and who finds himself for the first time on the shores of a sea. The manual sketches out for him a large number of ways of travelling about on or in water: swimming, by breast stroke, by crawl, by sidestroke, by back stroke and so on; canoeing; rowing; sailing in single-man dinghies;

snorkeling; scuba diving; and the last chapter of the book, on computer simulation, might even be considered as an introduction to mechanical propulsion in large surface vessels or submarines. The point is that we have not been pursuing one single course with a number of difficulties, as in the steeplechase. We have been taking a look at a variety of different ways of handling a kind of situation we are not used to, any more than a land dweller is used to handling the sea. Considerations of complex shapes of interactions of processes, of stabilities, traffic of information and instructions, games theories, forecasting, statistics and more classical scientific analyses, make up a collection of somewhat different tools, each more or less appropriate in particular circumstances, and when particular tasks are being attempted. As we become more adept in the uses of each particular tool, we shall presumably come to see how they complement one another to make up a flexible and powerful battery from which we can more or less automatically pick up the hammer or the mallet, the screw driver or the chisel, the plane or the spoke shave, according to the task in hand.

There are, of course, many complex systems in the world for which tools of these kinds may be useful. Their particular importance in this time in history, and the reason that they are being developed now although they have been so neglected in the past, is that mankind is quite suddenly coming to the vivid realization that he is in great danger of being swallowed up by what might be called the complex system to end all complex systems. History since World War II has been nothing but a series of problems: the Cold War which flared into actual military action only in a few rather peripheral places; then the population problem, the environment problems, the food problems, the urbanization problem, the energy crisis, transport getting so plentiful that it prevented itself from moving, leisure that turns into unemployment, affluence that becomes transmuted into inflation. Each one of these problems is complex enough. Population involves all the questions we discussed in the section on growth, and also, because the number of children born this year affects the number of people who will be bearing children twenty years later, it involves many of the interactions of sequences and networks of processes discussed in chapters 5 & 7; again, because having a baby now may mean that twenty years hence you have to provide a dowry for a daughter or you have a healthy son to look after you in your old age, it raises many of the problems which Games Theory tries to tackle. That is by no means the end of the complexities even of that one topic, and of course that topic does not stand alone. The population problem is closely tied up with the food problem, the urbanization problem, the traffic problem, the energy problem and so on. It is really hopeless to expect to deal successfully with any one of these complex problems on its own. Even if we had already attained much greater skill in handling these Tools for Thought about complex problems than we have in fact developed up to the present, what we are really confronting is a *complex* of *complexes*. This has been called the World Problematique. It is a formidable situation; but this is what the world is like at the present time. It is for this reason that the development of adequate Tools of Thought about Complex Systems is so overwhelmingly important.

# References and Suggested Reading

I do not know of any other book which covers this field, or even a large part of it. Perhaps John R. Platt's two books, *The Step to Man*, Wiley, 1966, and *Perception and Change*, University of Michigan Press, 1970, come as near to it as anything. A good general account of several modern methodologies is G. Polya, *How to Solve It*, Doubleday, 1957. A rather wordy, but cheap, collection of articles is *Systems Thinking*, edited by F. E. Emery, Penguin, 1969. Herbert A. Simon, *The Sciences of the Artificial*, deals with many of the topics in a fairly condensed way, particularly complexity, design, hierarchical organization and Games Theory.

Turning to particular chapters, it is obviously impossible to provide a short course of readings in philosophy which will appeal to all tastes; the choice is too enormously wide. I will content myself with recommending A. N. Whitehead, *Science and the Modern World*, Cambridge University Press, 1923, as a book which had a considerable influence on me and which I think is now unduly neglected, and will probably soon come back into favour.

For the special subject of 'fuzzy variables', an elementary account of recent developments is Rex Malik, 'Fuzzy Thinking', *New Scientist*, 18 October 1973. More sophisticated discussions are L. Zalek, 'The Logic of Fuzzy Sets', and E. C. Zeeman and O. P. Buneman, 'Tolerance Spaces and The Brain', in *Towards a Theoretical Biology* vol. 1, edited by C. H. Waddington, Edinburgh University Press, 1968.

On the side of moral philosophy, again anything like a representative selection is impossible here; but it is probably worth while drawing attention to some recent writings. On the issue of the alleged connection between Christianity and the exploitation of nature, a key article in the recent emphasis on this claim was L. White Jr, *The Historical Origin of our Ecological Crises*, *Science*, *155*, 1969, p. 1203. A more scholarly and, I think, sounder discussion is by John Black, in *The Dominion of Man*, Edinburgh University Press, 1970. For the 'counter-culture' and anti-science thesis, my favourite book is Philip Slater, *The Pursuit of Loneliness*, Beacon Press, 1970. Perhaps better known are two books by Theodore Roszak, *The Making of a Counter Culture* and *Where the Waste Land Ends*, both Doubleday Anchor, 1969 and 1970. Another book which has had a recent period in fashion is Charles Reich, *The Greening of America*. I have given my more general ideas in C. H. Waddington, *The Ethical Animal*, Chicago University Press, 1967.

For Chapter 2, 'Complexity', the books by Simon and Platt cited above are good general discussions. They could be supplemented by Stafford Beer, 'Managing Modern Complexity', in *Futures*, September 1970, and articles on handling information overload, by J. G. Miller and R. L. Meier. The actual data used as an illustration on page 36 are taken from J. Lukasiewicz, 'The Ignorance Explosion', *Trans. N.Y. Acad. Sci.*, 1972, p. 373.

For Chapter 3, on shapes, a modern classic on symmetry is Hermann Wey, *Symmetry*, Princeton University Press, 1952. *Module, Proportion, Symmetry, Rhythm*, edited by Gyorgy Kepes, Braziller, 1966, is also very good. A more professional account in a particular field, with good illustrations, is Ivan Bernal, Walter C. Hamilton and John S. Ricci, *Symmetry: a Stereoscopic Guide for Chemists*, Freeman, 1972. The illustration of the seventeen symmetry classes (4a.2) is taken from J. D. Bernal, 'Art and the Scientist', in *Circle*, which was a manifesto of the modern art group of Britain in the 1930s (Faber and Faber, 1937). The discussion of non-symmetrical shapes is largely based on a paper by Harry Blum, in *J. Theoretical Biology*. For a wider variety of methods with applications (including Blum's system) see 'Form and Pattern' in *Human Evolution* by Charles Ornard, University of Chicago, 1973.

For Chapter 3, 'Structures', there is a good short article by Philip Tabor, 'Structures of Organisation' in *Architectural Design*, May 1971. If you want a taste of the more rarefied lengths to which structural analysis has been carried recently in many fields, particularly in relation to anthropology and social affairs, Edmund Leach's short book on the prophet of the modern movement, *Lévi Strauss*, Fontana/Collins, 1970, is a good introduction, and *Structuralism: A Reader*, edited by Michael Lane, Cape, 1970, a solid work with contributions by many of the major authors, though rather concentrated on applications to linguistics.

Chapter 6. On biological growth, the major classic is D'Arcy Thompson, *On Growth and Form*, published, large parts of it are not so technical as so frightening, and a good many recent artists claim to have been influenced by it. I have a non-technical article about it in the book edited by Gyorgy Kepes referred to in the last paragraph but one. There are, of course, many books in the technical-biological literature, e.g. A. E. Needham, *Growth Processes in Animals*, Pitman, 1964, or (mainly about plants) J. T. Bonner, *Morphogenesis*, Princeton University Press, 1952; but there is rather little suitable for the general reader on the wider aspects of growth. Perhaps the early part of Denis Meadows' book, *The Limits to Growth*, is as good as any. On chain reactions, see John Platt's *Step to Man*.

Chapter 6, 'Feedback', and the first section of Chapter 7, 'Stable States', is what one might call 'conventional cybernetics'. This group of ideas had their origin in biology, and then spread into engineering and physics. Americans usually attribute their beginning to W. B. Cannon (major work 1932), Frenchmen to an even earlier physiologist, Claude Bernard (main work around 1870). The man who gets the credit for making the ideas influential in the modern world is the American mathematician Norbert Wiener, who coined the word 'cybernetics' – based on the Greek word for a steersman of a ship. His book *Cybernetics*, MIT Press, 1965, is well worth reading, but he was a bit too inclined to follow Greek examples; for instance, that of Archimedes, who rushed naked out of his bath into the street shouting 'Eureka' (I've found it), when he realized that the way to measure the volume of his very geometrically complicated body was to get into an absolutely full bath of water and measure how much overflowed. Wiener shouted 'Eureka' at least as loud as the traffic could take; but this, and another book of his, *The Human Use of Human Beings*, Avon, 1967, contain much worth anyone's while to read. For an introduction to the more formal analysis of sequences, networks, etc., Jagjit Singh, *Operational Research*, Penguin, 1968, is a good start, including the bibliography. For really subtle stuff about the steady states reached by networks, see H. Kacser, 'The Control of Flux', *Symp. Soc. Exp. Biol. 27*, 1973.

For lock-ins, see John Platt, 'Lock-ins and Multiple Lock-ins in Collective Behaviour', *American Scientist*, Summer 1969. Schismogenesis and double-bind are discussed, by the man who invented the ideas, in Gregory Bateson, *Steps to an Ecology of Mind*, Chandler and Paladin, 1973.

For the second section in Chapter 7, about steady flows, it is more difficult to give appropriate reading. The ideas are quite largely my own invention, and I coined the words 'chreod' and 'homeorhesis'. They both gelled into something fairly firm by the time of my *Strategy of the Genes*, Allen and Unwin, 1957. The notions have mostly been discussed in rather sophisticated ways, for example in the book by the French mathematician, René Thom, *Stabilité Structurelle et Morphogénèse*, Benjamin, 1972, due to appear shortly in English translation; or Jean Piaget, *Biologie et Connaissance*, translated, unfortunately not very clearly, as *Biology and Knowledge*, University of Edinburgh Press and University of Chicago Press, 1971. I have discussed them in more general contexts, for non-technical audiences, in *The Nature of Mind*, and *The Development of Mind*, Gifford Lectures for 1971/2 and 1972/3, Edinburgh University Press, 1972 and 1973. There is also a very clear and simple exposition by Christopher Zeeman, 'The Geometry of Catastrophe', *Times Literary Supplement*, 10 December 1971, and, with judicious skipping, his article 'Differential Equations for the Heartbeat and Nerve Impulse in *Towards a Theoretical Biology* vol 4, edited by C. H. Waddington, Edinburgh University Press, 1972, gives about as thorough an idea of what this new intellectual development is all about as anyone but a specialist is likely to need. The ideas about how to explore an epigenetic landscape are taken from a paper on the modelling of biological systems by I. M. Gel'fand and M. L. Tsetlin, published (in Russian) in the *Proceedings of the Soviet Academy*, 1969, translated by my daughter, Mrs McDuff.

On the classical scientific method in Chapter 8, the two books which everyone would claim as the classics of the present time are Karl Popper, *Logik der Forschung*, translated as *The Logic of Scientific Discovery*, or his more recent *Objective Knowledge*, Clarendon Press, Oxford, 1972, and Thomas S. Kuhn, *The Structure of Scientific Revolutions*, University of Chicago Press, 1962. Personally, I would add to these A. N. Whitehead, *Science and the Modern World*, referred to above, and if you have the time, the same author's *Concept of Nature* and *Principles of Natural Knowledge*, Cambridge University Press, 1925 and 1926. Anyone interested should also certainly read John Platt, *Strong Inference* in the *Step to Man*; there is an outstanding summary of the *Philosophy of Science* by Stephen Toulmin in the new edition of the *Encyclopedia Britannica*; and I have expounded my own views further in the Bernal Lecture 'The New Atlantis [of Bacon] Revisited', *Proc. Roy. Soc. Lond.*, 1965.

About statistics, there are a large number of books; none, to me, very exciting. But I'm probably jaundiced; as what I have written makes clear, I am not an *afficianado* of this particular methodology. But I think two good avenues to start exploring it in more depth would be M. J. Moroney, *Facts from Figures*, Penguin, 1964, and R. M. Cormack, *The Statistical Argument*, Oliver and Boyd, 1971.

For information theory, in Chapter 9, the main reference is Claude E. Shannon and Warren Weaver, *The Mathematical Theory of Communication*, University of Illinois Press, 1962, and at least the Introduction is fairly easy going. Probably better for the beginner is the complete number of the *Scientific American* which was devoted to Information and Communication in September 1966. For a simple introduction to giving instructions to computers, try Wilson Y. Gateley and Gary C. Bitter, *Basic for Beginners*, McGraw–Hill, 1970, but there are many other simple tests for other types of computer. The game of 'life' is discussed in the *Scientific American* for October 1970 and February 1971 and 'worms' in the same journal, November 1973. A main sophisticated text in this area is Michael Arbib, *Theories of Abstract Automata*, Prentice Hall, 1969.

For Chapter 10, *Operational Research* by Jagjit Singh covers a good deal of the ground, including statistics. About Games Theory in particular, it is worth reading 'The Use and Misuse of Game Theory', by Anatol Rapoport, in *Scientific American* for December 1962, and the same author's *Strategy and Conscience*, Harper Row, 1964. For some recent developments in this field, there is Nigel Howard, *Paradoxes of Rationality: The Theory of Metagames and Political Behavior*, MIT Press, 1971; but perhaps the review of it in *Science*, 11 May 1973, p. 395, will be enough for anyone but the specialist. The example of time budgeting is taken from an article by Carl Djerassi, 'Birth Control After 1984' in *Science* 149 941; 4 September 1970.

The method discussed here as meeting conflicting requirements is explained in Richard Levins, *Evolution in Changing Environments*, Princeton University Press, 1968. A more orthodox economist's view of uncertainty is Ruth P. Mack, *Planning on Uncertainty*, Wiley-Interscience, 1971. The account of participation of those planned for in the efforts of planners to satisfy them is based on Lawrence Halprin, *The RSVP Cycles: Creative Processes in the Human Environment*, Braziller, 1969. For Operational Research, an account of its origins and general character is given in my book *O.R. in World War II: Operational Research against the U-Boat*, which was written in 1946, but suppressed for security reasons till recently, Elek, 1973. More recent, and fairly simple accounts, are in the book by Jagjit Singh referred to above, and in Eric Duckworth, *A Guide to Operational Research*, Methuen, 1962.

Chapter 11, about technological forecasting, is based on a draft written by Robin Roy while he was working as one of my assistants in the

Einstein Professorship in the State University of New York at Buffalo in 1970. One of the best books about the subject is still one of the earliest thorough treatments of the subject, Erich Jantsch, *Technological Forecasting in Perspective*, O.E.C.D., Paris, 1967. Among the many other books, one might mention Robert U. Ayres, *Technological Forecasting and Long Range Planning*, McGraw–Hill, 1969, and Yehezkel Dror, *Design for Policy Sciences*, Elsevier, 1971. A readable summary of the subject was published as a special number of *Science Journal* in October 1967.

The classical example of an attempt to use some of these methods to forecast future technological developments is Herman Kahn and Anthony J. Wiener, *The Year 2000*, Macmillan, N.Y., 1967, and revised, Futures, Hudson, 1972. They need to be taken with a considerable pinch of salt. One short discussion which adds some perspective is Dennis Gabor, *Technological Forecasting in a Social Frame*, Science of Science Foundation, London, 1968; and there are many other discussions in such journals as *Futures*, *The Futurist*, etc.

˘ Finally, the technique of making models which can be put into computers is being extensively discussed, particularly by economists; see Jeremy Bray, *Decision in Government*, Gollancz, 1970, and by ecologists (e.g. J. Maynard Smith, *Models in Ecology*, Cambridge University Press, 1972). The attempt to model the world system centres around the short book by D. L. Meadows and others, *The Limits to Growth*, Potomac Associates for Club of Rome, 1971. There is an extensive controversial literature about both how its results should be interpreted (as predictions of what will happen, or arguments about what might happen if . . .?), and about the validity of the numerical values used. As a beginning of this, it is worth reading the discussions in *Nature*, 4 August 1972, and *Science* vol. 177; M. Thring's article 'The Equations of Survival', *New Scientist*, 1 March 1973; and Jeremy Bray, *The Politics of the Environment*, Fabian Society, London, 1972. The journal *Futures* devoted its whole number for February 1973 to an extended criticism by the Science and Society group at the University of Sussex, and this has been published as a book *Thinking about the Future*, Chatto and Windus, 1973. A new and much more thorough Mark II Club of Rome study has recently been published: M. Mesarovic and E. Pestel, *Mankind at the Turning Point*, Dutton, 1974.

# Index